THE WELL - CONNECTED DOG
A GUIDE TO CANINE ACUPRESSURE

Amy Snow
Nancy A. Zidonis

Technical Editor
Ella Bittel, Veterinarian

Cover Design: Catherine Connors

Illustrations: Carla Stroh

TALLGRASS
PUBLISHERS,
LLC

Published By: Tallgrass Publishers, LLC
                   Larkspur, CO

Copyright: ©1999 by Tallgrass Publishers, LLC
                   Larkspur, CO

Library of Congress Catalog Number - in progress
ISBN 0-9645982-4-8

1st Edition 1999, 4th Printing 2002
Printed in the United States of America

FOREWORD

The science of acupressure is based on the Taoist metaphysics of dynamic balance, harmony and Chi, the life force and its myriad manifestations, including conditions of disease. Chi is the term given to the subtle energy that is associated with the various meridians and acupressure points described in this book. It is synonymous with the life force, Shakti or Kundalini, of Eastern medicine and philosophy. In the process of applying acupressure to specific points, the Chi energy of the healer is transferred to the patient. This facilitates the release of blocked energy in the meridian through the acupoint and may help increase or decrease the energy level that is linked with various internal organs and neuro-hormonal functions.

Acupressure is a tool of "holistic" human and nonhuman animal medicine based on the neo-Taoist metaphysics and derivative bioethical principles for right living, that apprehends the sacred as wholeness and interdependence.

There are other tools of alternative veterinary medicine and companion animal health-care maintenance that accord with the bioethical principles of this new (and ancient) approach to improving animals' health and well-being. Much improvement is needed and will be achieved when certain bioethical principles that constitute the rights of all animals under our dominion become part of the heart and moral fabric of society. These principles are: right breeding (to avoid harmful diseases of hereditary origin); right socialization and rearing; right handling and understanding; right environment and nutrition. These are animals' basic rights and are our cardinal duties as their caretakers and custodians.

Acupressure is adjunctive and complementary. I would not advise immediately giving acupressure treatments until any violations or deviations from these bioethical principles are first considered in order to better determine the factors responsible for the animal's disease and the best course of treatment to follow. It would be very short-sighted not to consider if the animal is receiving right nutrition, for example, or if there is some underlying hereditary factor contributing to the animal's ill health and suffering.

Acupressure is not a panacea, but as this book affirms, many conditions will be significantly ameliorated by applying these alternative treatments. While I do not advocate pet owners doctoring their animal companions without professional approval and supervision if need be, owners can play a vital role in helping their animals cope with chronic degenerative diseases and during convalescence from some acute disease or surgery. I made this very clear in my 1981 book The Healing Touch. Furthermore, giving your animal companion a routine massage or a toning session of acupressure provides very important benefits that are part of the "holistic" approach to animal health care maintenance.

This book is a contribution to the necessary turn-around in our thinking about life and reactions toward disease and suffering. It is indeed a welcome and much-needed addition to the growing library of useful texts and manuals on companion animal care and health maintenance. There is additionally, benefit for those who discover the power of the healing touch. It is something that we can all give, and refine, and in the process we facilitate our own healing and wholeness as we relax, focus, and touch. Our blood pressure is likely to fall and we may begin to experience subtle energies, sensations, and feelings, as we resonate in an ever-deepening sympathy and empathy through the healing power of touch.

All healers become ever more aware, as their skills are refined, of how they must best deal with others' pain and suffering. Even when the beauty and sanctity of life have been defiled, when sentient beings are deliberately abused - a puppy beaten, a child raped by a parent, or any creature mentally and therefore spiritually harmed - the healer remains centered. Achieving such balance and centeredness is extremely difficult in these times when the less sensitive of our own kind cause so much suffering and manifest such contempt for life.

When California massage therapist Naomi Pettit trained me for certification as a human massage therapist, she advised me to become aware of my breath. And to pray as I breathed, first to be shielded and then to be able to feel where the healing energy - my Chi - should be directed. She signed my certificate when I was able to feel and deal with a sick patient - one of her students who had influenza - and help her feel well.

I realized that the healer's Chi is focused and sustained through prana - breath - and undivided attention. Attention divided between success and failure, uncertainty and hope, and training and feeling, is a soul divided and a spirit unrealized. The healer's composure, like a preying mantis or a Tai Chi Master, is centered in the eternal now.

This is our natural, feral state of consciousness and way of being, like any other animal. If we lose touch with this way - the Tao of our being, or our individual natures in Nature - we become disconnected, then out of balance, ill at ease, and so diseased.

In order to heal, healers must first heal their own wounds and face their own psychospiritual pathologies and mental and physical maladies. All sentient beings are part of the matrix of our existence, be they trees or bees. When we harm one being or an entire species or ecological community, we harm the life and sentient matrix of Chi, and therefore ourselves. This is the karmic, anthropogenic component of most diseased conditions, from cancer to catatonia, that afflict our species and many other species today. Some of these diseases have been called domestogenic and agricologenic diseases, like the pneumonia and arthritis of factory farmed animals; and the blights and infestations of apple, banana, corn, cotton, soybean, and other monoculture plantations, orchards and chemical fields now growing 70 million acres worldwide of genetically engineered crops and livestock feed, the harmfulness of which is only now being discovered and quantified. Others are diseases of "civilization and progress" - like obesity, anorexia, anxiety, ulcers, high blood pressure, neuralgia, migraine, drug addiction, homicide, rape, genocide and ecocide.

We should neither despair nor extinguish ourselves in rage over the stupidity, selfishness and arrogance of our species. We must simply survive, in spite of ourselves, and try to do whatever healing and prevention and alleviation of others' suffering that we may in the course of trying to stay in balance ourselves. These are difficult times.

I became more aware of the forces that threw me off balance when I first stopped eating animal products and attended Hatha yoga classes. I then became more aware of, responsible for, and in control of my own Chi. This did not make me a superior person or great healer. It simply made me a little more sensitive and mindful.

I remember learning about some great healers who were able to heal people, balance, and free their Chi, without ever having to touch them. I believe that St. Francis of Assisi, among a few other saints and sages, manifested this divine power through this mutual affinity with fellow creatures: Holy communion indeed.

I hope that readers will keep these thoughts and observations in mind, as they prepare to give acupressure treatments to their companion animals, and enjoy....and enjoin.

Dr. Michael W. Fox
Veterinarian and Author
Washington, D.C.

ACKNOWLEDGMENTS

We are grateful to our many dogs, past present and future, whose willingness to share our lives with us has made this book possible and meaningful. We hope this manual returns some of their generosity.

We thank Dr. Michael W. Fox for his contribution to this book and his many years of making the world better for animals and humans.

We are fortunate to have Ella Bittel, Veterinarian, provide expert technical editorial review. Ella is a holistic veterinarian and lives in California. She studied in Hanover, Germany and is certified by the International Veterinarian Acupuncture Society and the American Veterinary Chiropractic Association.

We greatly appreciate Carla Stroh's professional artistic talents and serving as our signature artist and illustrator. Thank you to Jan Jones for sharing her talent in photography.

We thank our friends for their patience, love and support during the process of creating this book. A special note of gratitude to Ann Zidonis, Erica Leah Pois and Marie Soderberg.

Courtesy of Crystal Glen Kennel, Fort Collins, CO

Table of Contents

Our connection

A dog is a dog. A dog is also our best friend, our child, our protector, helpmate, playmate, inspiration and connection to a simpler, loving world. We identify so much with dogs that we interpret their body language, expressions, and sounds in human terms. Most of us know exactly what our dogs think and feel at any given moment. Best of all, dogs and people truly enjoy each other's company.

The bond between our two species dates back thousands of years. Many authoritative books have been written about the origins of the domesticated dog. Scientists have studied canines from their bristly whiskers to the tips of their wagging tails. Behaviorists and trainers have produced volumes to help us enjoy our relationships and share our homes with our dogs. Rather than attempt to retell the historian's or the scientist's perspective of the domesticated canid, *The Well-Connected Dog: A Guide to Canine Acupressure* gives you and your dog an opportunity to understand and care for each other in an entirely different way.

Acupressure is an ancient healing art. This noninvasive, deceptively gentle treatment can profoundly impact both humans and animals. Dogs are extremely receptive to acupressure. Casework has shown consistently that acupressure can enhance your dog's comfort, emotional stability, and overall health. Specifically, acupressure can:

- Relieve muscle spasms
- Build the dog's immune system
- Release endorphins necessary to reducing pain
- Release natural cortisone to reduce swelling
- Enhance mental clarity required for focus in training and performance
- Resolve injuries more readily by removing toxins and increasing blood supply.

Modern medicine has begun to acknowledge the value of eastern healing modalities. Fortunately, we have the knowledge to make optimal use of both western and eastern approaches and techniques when caring for ourselves and our dogs. Given the growing awareness of the benefits of the ancient healing arts, more people are actively participating in their animals' well-being.

Acupressure does not substitute for veterinary medicine or animal chiropractic care. When your dog is ill or injured, we encourage you to consult your medical practitioner and get the assistance needed to resolve the physical injury or disease. Acupressure is an important avenue of treatment that complements western medicine.

We invite you to explore the realm of acupressure to return your dog's loving tail wags, service, and honest pleasure in being apart of your life. Dogs understand the language of touch. Having your attention is one of their greatest rewards. *The Well-Connected Dog* is a step-by-step guide to acupressure. This book offers you and your dog access to powerful healing and will contribute to deepening your mutual bond.

To bring the benefits of acupressure to you and your dog, we have distilled some of the essence of Traditional Chinese Medicine's (TCM) vast and complex body of knowledge. This book is a journey into the ancient healing arts. We hope this will be an unending adventure for you in learning to heal, share and care for your dog.

Beauty without Vanity,
Strength without Insolence,
Courage without Ferocity,
and all the Virtues of Man
without his Vices.

Lord Byron in memory of his cherished dog, Boatswain

chapter one

GOOD DOG, HEALTHY DOG

The human-dog connection is without comparison. This interspecies relationship started thousands of years ago when feral dogs risked living on the outskirts of human communities and began proving they could serve us. The canine motivation for serving human beings is the same now as it was then—their dinner bowls.

Seizing on their dogs' weakness for a good supper, we have "designed" dogs to fit our own needs. Their first jobs were related to human survival, such as guarding, herding, hunting, and performing military tasks. Through selective breeding, people created hunting dogs suited to the terrain with a predatory instinct to chase game in the specific locale. With astute breeding, we retained dogs' protective qualities while subduing their fearful attack reactions. Temperament, distinctive appearance, and a host of other traits were factored into their breeding so dogs would fill specific roles in human society.

Dogs are expected to adapt to our world. We breed them for our purposes. Through the years, we have expanded their roles significantly, adding different kinds of highly-trained jobs such as: search and rescue, drug-sniffing, k-9 police work, guides for the visually impaired, hearing-alert, seizure-alert, and public access dogs for the physically challenged. When training is not harsh or abusive, dogs love to work. Working dogs are active, challenged, and an important part of our lives.

We all enjoy having a companion dog greet us when we come home. Dogs are our most official greeters. If they have not been mistreated or neglected, they are

Nest Heads

Compliments of Steve Dickenson

friendly and responsive and they thoroughly relish every moment of our attention. We are lucky to have them.

Acupressure Enhances Connection and Health

As an ancient eastern healing art, acupressure has been used with animals for at least four thousand years. Dogs are highly attuned to acupressure. One of our own dogs, Shayna, had surgery on her lower spine when she was thirteen months old. Whenever she thinks someone might be willing to give her an acupressure treatment, she backs up with amazing accuracy to the right acupoint under the person's hand. Being both social and sensual, dogs are willing acupressure subjects.

Acupressure is a way to actively participate in your dog's health. By learning how to apply acupressure treatments, you can create a close partnership with your dog, which will contribute to years of quality companionship and performance. The relationship you build with your dog through acupressure treatments will enhance your dog's comfort, emotional stability, and overall health. The effects of acupressure have shown consistently the treatment's ability to release endorphins and natural cortisone which increases blood supply needed for healing and for enhancing mental focus.

By combining the ancient eastern healing arts, modern medicine, and loving good sense, you give something special and deeply caring to your dog. We ask our dogs to join us in our hectic lives—often not realizing how stressful their own lives are. Acupressure gives us a means to mitigate and reduce our dogs' stress and tend to their well-being.

When your dog is ill, injured, or experiencing a behavior disorder, you are encouraged to consult your veterinarian, animal chiropractor, or animal behaviorist, to receive the benefits of modern technological advancements. Western medicine, psychopharmacology, and animal behavioral sciences are effective avenues for resolving physical trauma, disease, and severe behavior problems. Acupressure augments western medicine and can alleviate the need for extreme treatments.

In practicing acupressure, as with other Traditional Chinese Medicine (TCM) disciplines, the practitioner considers all aspects of the dog's life and physical characteristics when assessing the dog's condition. We cannot separate the dog's health from his environment, the food he eats, how he spends his time, his amount of daily exercise, his physical traits, gait, response to sound, the look in his eye—everything that characterizes this particular dog's life. We view the dog and his life as a whole.

The Dog's Basic Needs

Dogs are very basic. Their needs are relatively simple. They require so little to be content; yet sometimes we forget to give them the simple things that help them have healthy, happy, and full lives. Perhaps it is because we have expected dogs to serve our needs for so long that we overlook theirs.

Good dogs are good because their needs are met. Good dogs have sufficient exercise, outdoor time, socialization with other dogs, play time, a clean place to play, consistent and caring contact with the caretaker and other humans, clean water, a natural, healthy diet, and positive, ongoing training. Every dog potentially is a good dog. Frankly, we have never met an inherently bad dog.

There are various reasons why dogs develop health and behavior problems. Some difficulties arise from breeding, some from human mishandling. Acupressure is not a cure-all; it cannot correct poor breeding practices, nor alone solve problems of depression, fear, or aggression brought on by poor handling. By using the acupressure techniques in this book, you can help your dog when he is in pain, injured, suffering from a dis-ease condition, or fearful and distressed.

Breeding and Physical Health

The American Kennel Club (AKC) recognizes about 150 breeds, although there are over 400 distinct breeds in the world. Selective breeding yields dogs that have all the attributes needed for a job description, such as companion, hunter, or guide dog. Unfortunately, sometimes genetics play tricks that can be harmful to the dog. For instance, some breeds have an hereditary predisposition to hip dysplasia, a malformation of the hip joint. This is a serious problem that can be very painful for a dog as he grows to mature size or when he develops an associated arthritic condition later in life.

Samson, a Rottweiler puppy, was diagnosed with severe hip dysplasia when he was ten months old. His humans elected to have surgery to correct the problem. Before and after the procedure to reshape the hip socket so that it cupped the femur, Samson received acupressure treatments to assure optimal health prior to surgery and to aid in the post-surgery healing process. Samson's recovery was much quicker than expected. The veterinary surgeon and his humans were amazed at how soon he went from total immobilization to his happy, active, natural puppy-self.

Golden Retrievers are perhaps the quintessential family dog. They are usually calm, gentle, easy to train, very sociable, playful with children, and fun loving. Most often they are open and honest, with handsome faces and soft coats. The Golden is such a popular breed that they are at risk of being over-bred, even though they are a relatively new breed (first AKC registration was accepted in 1932). Overbreeding can cause the loss of some of the very virtues desired in a dog. Irresponsible breeding can cause an undesirable temperament and physical weaknesses, such as hip dysplasia or other joint problems. Every breed has genetic quirks. Responsible breeders are careful to keep these in check by not breeding dogs that show evidence of undesirable traits.

The popularization of particular breeds already has caused untold suffering for millions of dogs. *101 Dalmatians* is a recent example of what happens when Hollywood gets into the act. Now, everyone wants a Dalmatian with their adorable spots and smart look. As puppies, they are like all puppies—irresistible. Whenever there is a popular breed, puppy mills start producing as many as they can, as fast as they can, to make as much money as possible.

Puppymill operators confine the dam to a small cage and breed her successively. The health of the dog is not considered; she is a puppy producing machine. There is no thought to her nutrition, fresh air, exercise, or any of the factors that create healthy offspring. The puppies are usually sold to pet shops, then to unsuspecting consumers. Popularization can be devastating to a breed, plus, many young dogs are put down in shelters after the novelty of having a puppy wears off.

When purchasing or adopting a puppy, it is suggested that you carefully research the background of the breeder and view both the sire and the dam. Even with a mixed-breed litter, it is important to see the puppy's parents. Becoming whole-heartedly attached to a puppy in less than five minutes is not unusual; however, it is heart-breaking when diseases emerge as the adorable creature grows to adulthood.

San Francisco boasts the best no-kill animal shelter in the world. Thanks to it's director, Richard Avansino, the San Francisco Society for the Prevention of Cruelty to Animals has created comfortable home-like accommodations for abandoned animals at Maddie's Pet Adoption Center. Visitors are welcome.

Breeding and Behavior

Selective breeding has produced definite personality tendencies. Originally, the temperament and behaviors were chosen carefully for a breed in relation to the type of work the dog would be expected to perform. Behavior problems arise when a dog's genetic make-up is not considered. When a hunting dog is confined to a small backyard with little variation in his environment, he is apt to develop behavior problems. If a friendly, social dog, like a Labrador Retriever, is isolated and unable to interact with other dogs, he can develop undesirable personality traits and behaviors.

Behaviorist, Dr. Nicholas Dodman, in his book *The Dog Who Loved Too Much: Tales, Treatments and the Psychology of Dogs*, gives another example: "Certain breeds are more likely to suffer from thunderstorm phobia than others. Northern breeds, such as Huskies and Samoyeds, and some larger breeds, such as Labradors, Retrievers, and German Shepherds, seem particularly prone."

Poor and unethical breeding practices have led to dogs that look good in a show ring but their temperament and manageability bear little resemblance to the original intent of the breed. Many a good breed are at risk of being lost to overbreeding.

Acupressure can help deal with many behavior problems but cannot overcome poor breeding. Acupressure can reduce a dog's anxiety, help build self-confidence, lower aggressiveness, help the dog be less fearful and more emotionally stable, and enhance his mental focus.

Handling and Behavior

The minute a puppy is born, he experiences some connection to human handlers. He senses how his mother feels about humans. His little nose picks up the scent of humans. Even with his ears flattened, he hears human voices and his little body feels the vibration of humans in the whelp-ing area. Like human infants, puppies begin to record and perceive the world at birth, if not earlier.

A puppy's initial experiences with humans and other dogs determines many things about his entire life. If a puppy's experience with humans from the start is loving, warm and gentle, the puppy is likely to be calm, confident, fun-loving, and easy to train. A puppy needs safe places to play and experiment with the environment. He needs to play with litter mates and other dogs to learn social behav-ior. Plus, he needs balanced natural foods to be healthy. Responding to the needs of a lively, growing puppy can be a challenge. Acupressure can support your efforts in giving the puppy what he needs energetically to be relaxed and willing to be trained, while building a strong body and healthy constitution. By giving your puppy acupressure treatments during this formative time, you are also building a strong bond that will last his entire life.

Trainers talk about how there is a brief window of training opportunity when a puppy is three to six months old. This is definitely an important span in a puppy's formative period; but dogs do continue to learn during their entire lives, as humans do.

If you adopt an older dog that is fearful, timid, aggressive, untrained, or not well adapted to the household, the dog can learn and change. Acupressure is particularly helpful in giving these dogs a different experience of being with humans. Looking at the human-dog connection, acupressure—along with other complementary therapies, such as aroma therapy, herbal supplements and homeopathy—can affect the dogs behavior regardless of age. It is difficult to desensitize a dog that was traumatized as a puppy; but through slow, careful, and consistent treatment many dogs return to trusting and loving humans.

As with breeding and the physical health of a dog, considering the initial intent of your dog's breed is very important to his emotional, energetic, and general well-being. Hunting-sporting dogs, and working-herding dogs need a lot of exercise and outside time. If you are unable to provide outside running space, plus time and attention to train and enjoy the breed, you might reconsider the type of dog you want. No amount of training, acupressure, or other complementary therapies can make up for a dog's basic living needs.

A well-meaning, but misguided, neighbor of ours kept her young Australian Shepherd locked in the basement during the day while she was at work. She thought he would stay out of trouble, be safe, and have room to move around in the dark, little basement during her ten-hour work day. The backyard was not enclosed. The only time Travis was able to get outside to take care of toileting and exercise needs was when she took him on a lead. By the time Travis was two years old, he was out of control. He barked constantly, spun in circles almost continuously, and was extremely timid around other dogs and humans. It was sad to see the fine, healthy little fellow in such a sorry state.

Australian Shepherds are outdoor working dogs. Their genetic hard wiring determines that every ounce of them craves miles and miles of running and herding. The Aussie is known for physical agility, keen senses, ability to learn from experience around herding animals, and quick response to commands. They are not meant to be confined in a basement, alone, day in and day out. Few humans tolerate solitary confinement; how could anyone believe a dog can survive such an experience? No wonder Travis developed serious behavior problems.

Dogs are happiest when they are doing what they were bred to do. Some dogs enjoy living in a small apartment with only three to four walks a day. You can find a dog to suit almost any lifestyle, although they always require the basic needs of any living organism.

Most of us who work with dogs are aware that the greatest contributing factors to their health and behavior problems is that humans do not fully understand their needs. In urban and suburban environments, dogs are often isolated, lonely, overweight, under-stimulated, and rarely get enough exercise. In rural areas, dogs still have roles to fill; they are outside most of the time and are part

---

Dog Protection Resources

Sometimes dogs need our help and protection. The first line of assistance in the case of neglect or abuse is your local animal shelter or animal control. There are many volunteer animal rescue groups in most communities as well. If there are no animal protection services in your area, every state government in the United States has an animal welfare office. State governments are responsible for the regulation of pet stores. The United States Department of Agriculture oversees commercial breeding, brokering and distribution of animals including companion animals. Publicly funded resources often have limited staff causing their ability to respond to vary. Another resource is:

The Humane Society of the United States (HSUS):
Website: www.hsus.org.
General: 202.452.1100
Disaster Services: 301.258.3101

If you suspect a local kennel or backyard breeder is operating a puppymill notify:

United States Department of Agriculture,
Animal and Plant Health Inspection Services:
General Website: www.usda.gov
APHIS Website: www.aphis.usda.gov
General: 301.734.4980

American Kennel Club:
General: 919.233.9797

of their humans' lives. Country dogs are more likely to live longer, healthier, and richer lives than their city cousins.

Humans rule the dogs' world. We are totally responsible for their health and welfare. Dogs look to us for just about everything. We are their access to all of their survival and pleasure needs: food, physical comfort, attention and affection, contact with other dogs, going outside to play, sniff and toilet. These animals willingly perform tasks and give us their energy, love, forgiveness, and furry presence in exchange for our care of them. Acupressure is a sustaining and caring language of touch that dogs understand and fully appreciate.

Dogs and humans have something important in common. We are both social beings. Our mutual social need is the common denominator that links us, fostering a bond that makes our destinies' inseparable. The domestic dog has been at our side for much of human history and probably will remain so until we are no longer here. Dogs contribute so much to our lives. Now, through the loving and healing touch of acupressure, we can return the gift.

chapter two

TRADITIONAL CHINESE MEDICINE

Overview

Your dog will not understand a word of this book, but he definitely will understand how good he feels. He will know your intent of caring and healing. Since it is important for your dog to think you are the smartest person in the world, we will give you a brief overview of the concepts that underlie acupressure.

Acupressure connects you and your dog with natural healing. The source of acupressure lies in Traditional Chinese Medicine (TCM). Fully understanding and knowing TCM takes years of in-depth study and practice. It is a highly complex system that is both precise and flexible. Studying TCM is a rich and poetic experience that opens you to new sensations and concepts. Grasping some of the basic concepts will facilitate your ability to perform acupressure treatments on your own dog. The following discussion is a framework for: 1) how and why acupressure can balance your dog's energy; (2) the meridian system involved; and (3) how acupressure works to support your dog's optimum health, joy in life, and performance.

TCM treats the mind-body-spirit as a single entity in harmony with nature and the environment. The Chinese view the body—human or canine—as an intricate and interdependent system in which all aspects of internal life and external environment are intimately intertwined. Health is when the body-mind-spirit is in a state of harmony and in balance with external influences.

TCM developed as a preventive form of treatment. Originally, it was used to maintain the health of livestock, a valuable resource in China. Approximately 4,000 years later, practitioners are still being trained to identify disharmonies, or imbalances, in body energies before physical symptoms of an imbalance can manifest. Despite the tremendous healing powers of TCM, doctors in ancient China were paid only when their clients remained healthy. If a client became ill, it was a disgrace to the practitioner and payment was not expected.

In ancient China, the TCM practitioner approached healing from many levels and had highly sophisticated healing arts from which to draw. Techniques included dietary therapy, exercise, meditation, herbs, acupuncture, and acupressure. The practitioner's job was to observe the patient from many perspectives, then select the appropriate healing modalities and assist clients in integrating these into their lifestyles.

The TCM healing arts share a number of concepts. Following is a list with brief descriptions of the basic tenets that are common to all. We will explore these concepts in more depth and explain how they relate to the practice of acupressure.

Chi Energy	The life force energy infused in everything (pronounced *Chee*).
Yin/Yang	The representation of opposite but complementary qualities that are interdependent and exist in a constant state of dynamic balance.
Meridian System	A one-network system through which Chi energy is carried to all parts of the body.
Acupoints	They are analogous to pools of energy located along the meridians that are used to balance energy.
Eight Guiding Principals	Eight general patterns that assist the TCM practitioner in recognizing the causes of a disharmony in the flow of Chi through the meridian system.
Five Phases of Transformation	A complex conceptual framework that describes five natural phases of transformation. This theory provides an understanding of the true "checks and balances" that exist on earth and within living bodies. It identifies the building, or Creation Cycle; along with its counterpart, the Controlling or breaking-down Cycle. In acupressure, the Five Phases of Transformation are used to indicate how to balance energy and maintain or restore health and well-being.
Balancing Energy	Manipulation of energy to restore harmony and balance.

Chi Energy

The cornerstone of TCM is the life force energy called *Chi*. In eastern thought, Chi pulses through all life forms and is present in all of nature. Chi is the basis of everything that exists, including mineral, vegetable, and animal. Chi is the vital, dynamic force that controls harmony through constant transformation and conversion of matter and energy in a living body. We impact the total Chi available to us and our dog-friends by the quality of the lifestyles we create. If we eat good food, breathe clean air, exercise and create a positive environment, we help to preserve and create our Chi energy. It is exactly the same for our canine counterparts. Good quality nutrition and natural foods, proper exercise and a natural lifestyle, help our dogs have strong and balanced Chi, creating an environment for good health and healing.

Many levels and types of Chi in human and canine bodies are always working in concert. Different forms of Chi are identified by their locations and purposes. However, all the different types and forms of Chi are only one Chi, which merely exhibits itself in different forms.

It is important to note that when TCM refers to an organ, such as the lung or spleen, the reference is to the entire organ system affected by the organ. That is, when the lung is discussed in TCM terms, it means the lung's function in relation to the whole body. For the purposes of this manual, we discuss only the major forms of Chi and how they relate to the overall well-being of your dog.

Source Chi is given to offspring at conception and is the basis for Kidney Chi. It is stored at the Source Points of each meridian. This Chi is closely related to essence, or *Jing*, and is the hereditary Chi each animal receives at birth. Source Chi is the foundation of all Yin and Yang energies in a body. Every individual human and dog is born with a fixed amount of life force energy. Source Chi can be depleted by illness, poor nourishment, and an unhealthy environment. Source Chi lessens over time until death.

Through careful breeding practices or natural selection, and a healthy lifestyle of the dam and sire, every puppy starts out with a healthy amount of Source Chi. Since Source Chi is not replenishable, it is up to the dog's human to provide a wholesome diet and healthy lifestyle throughout the dog's life. Puppymill puppies often come into the world with too little Source Chi to sustain them and they are likely to fall prey to dis-ease.

Chest Chi is extracted from the air we breathe. Lungs inhale clean Chi, transforming it for the body's use and exhale stale, spent Chi. This continuous exchange and extraction of Chi keeps the body's physiological processes functioning properly. Exercise adds to the strength of the body's lung capacity. Most dogs need far more physical exercise than they get each day. They thoroughly enjoy playing and chasing other dogs and human friends while breathing clean air.

Since few dogs are able to be the hunters, guard dogs, or herders they originally were intended to be, people are devising a number of new sports for dog athletes. Flyball and Agility Training are two new dog sports. Canine Companions for Independence featured a Pet-a-Thalon at a recent Run-Walk-Roll Fund-raiser in Colorado Springs, Colorado. The Pet-a-Thalon consisted of a large agility course with many food, noise and visual distractions, requiring the dogs to be athletic and highly trained to compete. Fetch, frisbee, and field-trial, along with other dog and human sports, build Chest Chi.

Food Chi is derived from food and drink. It is released in the stomach after the digestive process changes food into body nutrients. Food Chi has a major role in supplementing the types of Chi that are not inborn but can be created during the dog's lifetime. This is why TCM attributes great importance to the quality and quantity of food that nourishes the body's energy.

Although descended from carnivores, dogs are omnivores, like us. They can eat what we eat and derive the same benefits we do from eating a balanced natural diet. A young veterinarian started her practice in a lower economic urban neighborhood on the west coast. She thought her clientele would be poorly nourished and suffering from diseases in advanced age, more than in more privileged areas. To her surprise, the companion animals basically were very healthy and lived into old age with vigor. She could only attribute the animals' good health to their diet of table scraps of beans, rice, corn meal, meats, and a variety of vegetables. Most of these cats and dogs had never eaten commercial animal food and definitely were very healthy.

> Giving your dog a large soup bone is good for him. Dogs both need and like to chew. It keeps their teeth and gums clean and strong. Also, a real bone keeps him busy and happy for hours.

Commercial dog food manufacturers are not bound by food standards or regulations in most countries. To say in advertising that their food is "balanced" or "natural" means very little. If you are feeding your dog commercially packaged or canned food, for your dog's benefit, we suggest you investigate higher quality foods at your local specialty pet store. Ideally, consider preparing you dog's meals at home, or blending a better packaged product with home-cooked meals.

Quite a few dog nutritionists, veterinarians, and top breeders are recommending a diet of raw food for excellent growth and health. There are many new dog nutrition books and natural pet publications available to review and learn more about a healthy diet for your dog. Some of these books are listed in the Bibliography section.

Protective Chi defends the body against harmful external forces. This Chi is the greatest Yang manifestation in the body. It travels within the chest and abdominal areas, and courses between the skin and muscles. Protective Chi governs the sweat glands and pores, protects skin and hair and keeps the organs warm. When Protective Chi is abundant, a strong defense system exists, keeping the body safe from harmful outside influences and diseases.

Protective Chi is directly responsible for your dog's immune system. Unfortunately, more "human" diseases are now seen in pets. Cancer, heart problems, and allergies are examples of the diseases that are becoming common in the dog population. Strong Protective Chi can destroy external pathogens and restore balance in the body, thus helping your dog avoid disease.

Meridian Chi is transported through invisible yet very real, pathways of the meridian system. Chi is constantly carried to the organs and creates an harmonious functioning of all aspects of the body. It travels through the body every twenty-four hours.

As a touch technique, acupressure works with Meridian Chi to restore the Yin-Yang balance of organ systems, allowing the body to restore and maintain health. By using touch techniques, we remove energy blockages in the meridian pathways so the Chi flows smoothly. We can strengthen, or tonify, a deficient flow of Chi energy through the meridian channels to enhance the movement. When an excessive amount of Chi energy is present, we can sedate, or disperse, the excess Chi as it flows through the meridian pathways.

Chi circulating through the human or canine body performs five major functions:

- Generates body warmth
- Protects the body from external harmful forces
- Governs the retention of body substances
- Creates all body movement; it is the source of voluntary and involuntary movement
- Serves as the basis of organ functions; for example, derives nutrients from food or air, and transforms and transports substances.

When performing an acupressure treatment on your dog, you are manipulating the flow of Chi through his body. Step-by-Step Acupressure Treatment, Chapter Three, offers detailed information regarding Meridian Chi and acupressure techniques.

Aspects of Chi

Chi energy, or life force energy, has different aspects. *Shen* represents the spirit aspect of Chi. *Jing* refers to the *life essence* or material aspect of Chi. These fundamental substances are an integral part of Chi and cannot be separated. To the TCM practitioner, Shen and Jing are real, just as a leg and arm are to a western medical practitioner.

Shen is the creative process that gives rise to thought, emotion, and consciousness. Some people do not believe that dogs think and have emotions; but those of us who are "dog people" know they do. Albeit, a dog's thought process may be simple and primitive, but there is much evidence—anecdotal and scientific—that dogs think and make choices. Any human who has a beloved dog will not hesitate to tell you that his or her dog has a full range of emotions from utter joy to heart-stricken grief. Dogs definitely are conscious of themselves and the world around them. People who do not know dogs often assume we are anthropomorphizing our dogs' behaviors. They are simply wrong.

Shen is primarily given to the fetus from both parents, stored in the heart and

Courtesy of Crystal Glen Kennel, Fort Collins, CO

revealed in the eyes. Shen reflects the interaction of essence and Chi. When the spirit is not balanced, the eyes appear clouded, dull, or vacant. You can tell when your dog is not in full spirit and complete health by looking into his eyes. The harmonious flow of Shen is essential to good health. It needs to be consistently nourished and revitalized.

Regular acupressure treatments help support and renew a dog's Shen. Acupressure along the Heart Meridian can help replenish the spirit of a depressed, or abused animal. Many things contribute to replenishing a dog's Shen, such as taking him to a natural environment to run in grassy fields with dog buddies, or scamper after sea gulls and bark at the waves on a shore. Dogs need to reconnect with their natural selves regularly to sustain and build Shen.

Dog's love to play with other dogs and with you—with frisbees, balls, bones, anything. Making sure your dog's love of play stays alive and vital will go a long way to assuring that his Shen energy is healthy.

Combined with Source Chi, Jing, or life essence determines the development of each dog's constitution. Jing is regarded as the material, tangible basis of Chi. Jing Chi can be thought of as genetic capability. A puppy's dam and sire may be sturdy Bull Mastiffs; but if the puppy does not receive quality food and exercise to create Food and Lung Chi, the puppy will not reach full potential. Given a healthful, nurturing environment and nourishing food, puppies develop well and attain their genetic potential of Jing.

Jing energy, also called the Source of Life, is stored in the kidneys. It has a fluid nature and circulates throughout the body, along with Chi. Jing determines growth, reproduction, and development. Jing is involved in producing *marrow*. In TCM, *marrow* is broadly defined; it is the substance common to bones, bone marrow, the spinal cord, and the brain. Given this concept of *marrow*, Jing determines physical and constitutional strength, while also impacting concentration and memory.

The fixed quantity of the inherited portions of Source Chi and Jing are the basis of the congenital constitution of the dog. The non-inherited portion of Chi is impacted by everyday lifestyle, including exercise, food, and stress level. The best way to positively affect your dog's Jing is for him to have a balanced lifestyle. For your dog, this translates to fun, challenging exercise, rest, a natural balanced diet, and healthy living conditions.

Maintaining a balanced flow of Chi, or life force energy, in spirit and physical form is absolutely essential to having a healthy dog. The demands we place on dogs to live in our environment causes them stress. A city apartment or a suburban backyard is not a dog's natural habitat. The domesticated canine is a unique hybrid of a natural canine and human-dependent anomaly. Consistent acupressure treatments offer dogs relief from some of the stress of living in our world; but it must be combined with all of the good things that our four-legged friends need.

Yin and Yang

Chi energy, in its many forms and functions, is a dynamic balance between two opposing forces. The concept of *Yin* and *Yang* is fundamental to TCM. Theoretically, there is a constant flow between two polarities called Yin and Yang. Within the singular entity of Chi, Yin and Yang are constantly moving and flowing from harmony to disharmony, balance to imbalance. They are opposite of each other and, thus, mutually interdependent; neither can exist without the other. Yin and Yang are constantly in a state of flux, so the increase of one creates the consumption of the other, maintaining balance.

The Yin component of Chi is associated with the maintenance and structure of matter. Yang is associated with movement and function. Although the forces of Yin and Yang are not really distinct, they are most clearly differentiated at the extremes. For example, day is thought of as Yang, night as Yin. In this example, each is clearly defined. As day approaches night, or dusk, the distinction between Yin and Yang becomes less clear. It is here that we see the reality of one dynamic force. Yin and Yang are often represented as opposites. Some of the attributes are:

	YIN	YANG
In the world	Rest	Excitement
	Night	Day
	Lower	Upper
	Solid	Hollow
	Moon	Sun
	Negative	Positive
In the body	Chest/abdomen	Spine/back
	Female	Male
	Nourishing Chi	Protective Chi
	Interior of the body	Surface of the body
	Weak sounds	Loud bark
In disease	Chronic	Acute
	Gradual onset	Rapid onset
	Cold	Heat
	Lies curled up	Lies stretched out
	Loose stools	Constipation
	Not thirsty	Thirsty
	Profuse, light urination	Scanty, dark urination

In a healthy body, Chi circulates through the meridian system channels in an ongoing and self-regulating balance. In an unhealthy body, Chi is not in balance, causing dysfunction. The meridian pathways may be blocked, congested, or stagnated, depending on the indicators or evidence the body is demonstrating. A dysfunction along the meridian pathways reduces your dog's self-regulating, energy-balancing capabilities and can cause a condition of excess or deficient Yin or Yang. Acupressure treatments work to restore the balance of the Chi's Yin/Yang force in your dog's body and to promote healing.

Meridian System - Energy Pathways

Chi energy, in its various forms and functions, provides life and a self-regulating balancing system for a healthy body. The meridians are a network-like channel system that transport Chi to all areas of the body, supplying life force energy. The meridian system:

 ▸ Moves Chi energy and balances Yin and Yang
 ▸ Reflects signs of disharmony or imbalance
 ▸ Resists external and internal pathogens
 ▸ Regulates conditions of excess and deficiency

PARTIAL MERIDIAN SYSTEM CHART

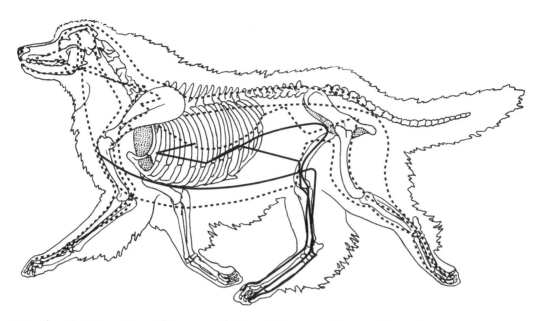

Twelve Major Meridians and Two Extraordinary Vessels

Each of the twelve major meridians is associated with an organ system, transmits Chi, and maintains the balance of the body's systems. The meridians are paired in Yin and Yang couples known as sister meridians. The twelve major organ system meridians are:

YIN	YANG
Lung	Large Intestine
Kidney	Bladder
Liver	Gall Bladder
Heart	Small Intestine
Pericardium	Triple Heater
Spleen	Stomach

There are also eight Extraordinary Vessels or pathways that connect and collect Chi from the twelve major meridians. Unlike the major meridians, these are not linked directly to the twelve organ systems. The Extraordinary Vessels are extremely important because they supplement interactions among the twelve major meridians. They also act as reservoirs for the major meridians by absorbing or transferring energy to the twelve major meridians, as needed. For the scope of this book, we discuss only the Extraordinary pathways of the Governing and Conception Vessels, which are the most well-known of the Extraordinary Vessels.

The Governing Vessel is known as the *Sea of Yang Channels*. It influences all of the Yang meridians and is used to *tonify* (enhance or strengthen) the body's Yang energy. The Governing Vessel nourishes the brain and spine. Its pathway runs from the anus to the top of the lip on the dorsal, top-side, midline of the dog.

The Conception Vessel is known as the *Sea of Yin Channels*. It influences all of the Yin meridians. The Conception Vessel is very important for the reproductive system of a dog, particularly a bitch. It influences her estrous cycle, fertility, pregnancy, and conception. The Conception Vessel's pathway runs from the dog's chin down through the legs, along the mid-line of the chest and belly to just below the anus.

Acupressure and Acupoints

As a revered TCM healing modality, acupressure is similar to acupuncture but does not use needles to stimulate the acupoints along the meridians and other locations. Experience has shown that it is not necessary to penetrate the surface of the skin to obtain the desired energy-balancing effect.

There are over 350 acupoints located along the meridians, and more than 250 non-meridian points. Many of these points are located in valleys of the body between muscles and bones. The Chi flows through the meridian channels and is accessible to manipulation through acupressure. When stimulated, the acupressure points along the meridian impacts the flow of Chi energy. During an accupressure treatment, pressure is applied to specific acupoints that either *tonifies* (increases) or *sedates* (decreases) Chi energy, as needed to balance the body and allow healing.

A comprehensive discussion of the acupoints, their location and purpose, are described in Chapter Five, Canine Acupoints. Acupressure treatment techniques for balancing energy through point work are described in Chapter Three, Step-by-Step Canine Acupressure Treatment.

Indicators

TCM is a highly refined and flexible system for understanding the body-mind-spirit as a single entity. Although we have transposed the ideas to the canine body, with some reasonable modifications, the basic concepts are the same. TCM strives to determine the underlying cause of an ailment by looking at the entire being from as many perspectives as possible. The practitioner discerns fundamental patterns that reveal the root cause of the dysfunctional condition before the course of treatment is developed. TCM practitioners most often use the Eight Guiding Principals and the Five Phases of Transformation (also known as the Five Element Theory) to understand the causes of an ailment. For the purposes of this manual, we introduce only the broad concepts behind the theories. The depth and complexity of identifying illnesses and treatments would require a book many times the size of this one.

Eight Guiding Principals

The Eight Guiding Principals, *Ba-gang*, are a further extension of Yin and Yang. As the physical, tangible evidence of Yin and Yang, they provide a method of conceptualizing and distinguishing different patterns.

The Eight Guiding Principals	
Yin	Yang
Interior	Exterior
Deficiency	Excess
Cold	Hot

The practitioner analytically observes the body by using all of his or her senses and knowledge to recognize the evidence of the Eight Guiding Principals. To identify certain patterns, the practitioner gathers historical, current, and lifestyle information about the human or dog. Knowing the location, quality, and extent of the eight opposite conditions gives the practitioner a way to clarify and organize the relationship between particular clinical signs.

For example, lethargy and physical weakness in your dog indicate a pattern of Yin deficiency. To make a precise treatment determination, the TCM practitioner assesses the body's whole condition by observing physical attitude, confirmation, areas of swelling, appearance of the skin and coat; smelling any unusual odors, and listening to body sounds; noting strength of vocalization (bark). The practitioner then checks particular acupressure points to see if, to the touch, they are hot or cold, indented or protruding, spongy or dense, painful or benign. Once the practitioner has performed a thorough examination and asked questions about the dog's current condition, lifestyle and history, the practitioner discovers the distinguishing pattern, *bian-zheng*, and is able to prepare a treatment plan.

Another example: hard lumps, swelling or dense tissue mass may indicate an excessive Yang condition. Soft lumps, swelling and spongy tissue mass may indicate an excessive Yin condition. In either case, the TCM practitioner continues to observe, collect information, check points, and use other indicators in order to fully understand the course of treatment required.

The Five Phases of Transformation

METAL

WATER

WOOD

FIRE

EARTH

The Five Phases of Transformation *(Wu Xing)*, also called the Five Element Theory, brings another level of understanding to the underlying basis of acupressure as a healing art. The Five Phases offer a deeper explanation of how Chi interacts, balances, and supports all life forms and the world as we know it. This book briefly touches upon the intricacies of the Five Phases, since they are one of the most significant conceptual foundations of TCM. Many other books are devoted to narrow slices of the subject because The Five Phases of Transformation is such a large body of knowledge.

Metaphorically, the Five Phases are identified as: Metal, Water, Wood, Fire and Earth. Sometimes referred to as elements, these Phases are primal forms that are the basis of all that exists in life. Each Phase, or element, is part of a larger, ordered transformational phase or cycle of existence in which nothing is static. The Creation Cycle, clockwise around the circle, is the building or growth cycle and represents a continuous flow of nourishing energy. Unending growth would cause an exponential compounding of energy from one phase to another, resulting in a dangerously extreme imbalance. The Control Cycle counteracts the Creation Cycle, constantly interacting to restore balance and harmonious synchronicity among all things.

Creation Cycle diagram

Traditional Description of the Creation Cycle:

Fire creates Earth - Ashes of fire add to earth.

Earth creates Metal - Adding earth creates metal.

Metal creates Water - Metal separates, allowing water to flow.

Water creates Wood - Water nourishes the growth of wood.

Wood creates Fire - Wood fuels fire.

Control Cycle Diagram

Traditional Description of the Controlling Cycle:

Fire controls Metal - Heat of fire melts metal.

Metal controls Wood - Metal chops wood.

Wood controls Earth - Roots of trees grow through earth.

Earth controls Water - Earth dams water.

Water controls Fire - Water dowses fire.

Complete Creation and Controlling Cycle Diagram

The Five Phases of Transformation is a conceptual framework that describes and defines the changes and relationships that exist in all of nature, including animals. The Phases are associated with the seasons, stages of transformative existence, climate, Yin and Yang organ systems, body tissue, geographic direction, predominant emotion, taste, smell, sense organ, color—everything!

21

FIVE PHASES OF TRANSFORMATION CORRESPONDENCE CHART					
	WOOD	**FIRE**	**EARTH**	**METAL**	**WATER**
TRANSITION	Birth	Growth/Creation	Maturity	Harvest	Storage
SEASON	Spring	Summer	Late Summer	Fall	Winter
CLIMATE	Windy	Hot	Wet/Humid	Dry	Cold
DIRECTION	East	South	Center	West	North
COLOR	Green	Red	Yellow	White	Blue
EMOTION	Anger	Joy	Sympathy/Worry	Grief	Fear
SENSORY ORIFICE	Eyes	Tongue	Mouth	Nose	Gentials/Ears
SMELL	Rank	Burning	Fragrant/Sweet	Putrid	Rotten
GOVERNED PART OF BODY	Tendons & Ligaments	Vascular System	Muscles & Lymph	Skin & Body Hair	Bones & Marrow
MERIDIANS	Liver & Gall Bladder	Heart & Small Intestine Pericardium Triple Heater	Spleen & Stomach	Lung & Large Intestine	Kidney & Bladder

The Five Phases provide essential information for the acupressure practitioner by directing the selection of appropriate meridians needed to rebalance and restore harmony between the internal and external worlds. Each set of meridians is associated with one of the Five Phases. The elements and their corresponding Yin/Yang meridians are:

ELEMENT	MERIDIAN	
	Yin	**Yang**
Wood	Liver	Gall Bladder
Fire	Heart	Small Intestine
	Pericardium	Triple Heater
Earth	Spleen	Stomach
Metal	Lung	Large Intestine
Water	Kidney	Bladder

Human and canine bodies are microcosms. We are composed of the same elements as the rest of the world. The Five Phases are always present in our bodies, by way of our organs and the meridians they impact. If Chi energy is blocked or imbalanced while traveling through the body, dysfunction and disease can manifest. Using the conceptual base of the Eight Guiding Principals and Five Phases, a practitioner can identify:

(1) exactly where the blockage has occurred; (2) if the energy is deficient or excessive; and, (3) which meridians and acupoints need to be manipulated. The result of the acupressure treatment is that the blockage is resolved and the energy can flow freely, allowing the body to heal.

For example, skin problems in your dog could indicate a deficiency in the Lung and/or Large Intestine Meridians (see Correspondence Chart for Governed Part of the Body). To identify points for tonifying or strengthening these meridians, the practitioner looks at the Creation Cycle—Earth creates, or strengthens, Metal. The Earth points within the Lung and Large Intestine meridians—Lu 9 and LI 11—stimulate these points and, thus, strengthen the skin.

Another example: if a bitch is cycling excessively, look at the Kidney Meridian to sedate the cycling activity (see Correspondence Chart for Orifices). The estrous cycle is partially a function governed by the Kidney Meridian, which is a water element. To "control" this, look at the Control Cycle—earth controls water. The practitioner then considers sedating the earth points in the Kidney and Bladder meridians, Ki 3 and Bl 54, to disperse the excess energy. (Note: Lu 9, LI 11, Ki 3, and Bl 54 are examples of Command Points. Classification of points is discussed further in Chapter Five, Canine Acupoints.)

Five Phases and Qualities

The Five Phases represent distinct physical qualities and characteristics; they also point to attributes of personality and temperament. Dogs can be thought of as an expression of a certain element. Any breed or natural selection dog can be identified as having predominant physical constitutions and temperaments.

Metal Dog

Dogs with balanced "metal" constitutions appear to be quick learners and have even-tempered natures. They demand a sense of fairness in training and put forth tremendous effort when treated fairly. Their body type is angular, lean, and strong. These dogs show a quiet maturity. They have a confident nature that may seem detached, serious, and even sad at times. These dogs like a sense of orderliness and predictability. Scent Hounds and their smaller Terrier cousins, and other Hunting-Gun dogs are apt to be Metal Dogs.

Water Dog

Dogs with a balanced "water" constitution exhibit the physical qualities of a strong, dense, large-boned body. Balanced Water Dogs have beautiful, shiny, healthy coats. They tend to be very observant and they like to evaluate situations. They may display tension or a healthy anxiety when under pressure. In the wild, this canine is seen as a survivor, self-sufficient, and resilient. We may think of a "water dog" as having webbed paws and keen retriever instincts, but this is not the Five Phases of Transformation concept of a Water Dog, though in some cases it fits. Chesapeake Bay and Labrador Retrievers fit our current and TCM descriptions of a Water Dog. The Gun Dog, Boxer, Bull Dog, Bull Mastiff also have evident Water Dog characteristics.

Wood Dog

Wood Dogs often appear energetic yet move somewhat stiffly. With a quality of determination, they push beyond apparent limits and are seen as independent. They are often impatient and have a very competitive nature. Wood dogs are probably the working dogs of any breed or natural selection. Sight hounds, livestock dogs and larger Spitz-type dogs, like Elkhound, Keeshond, and Akita also can be Wood Dogs; these dogs behave best with experienced handlers.

Fire Dog

The Dalmatian was bred to be a coach dog but has had the honor of becoming known as the "Fire House Dog". However, this is not what we mean in TCM terms by Fire Dog. A dog with a balanced "fire" constitution exhibits a joyful and vibrant personality. He is charismatic, playful, and friendly. The Fire Dog is fun, easy to train, and athletic. His intelligence and eagerness to learn make him a quick study for any type of training. He enjoys retrieving and carrying things in his mouth. His warm, gentle nature endears him to people and other animals. He wins friends effortlessly. This is the temperament of many breeds and natural selection dogs, including Labrador and Golden Retrievers, and Livestock Dogs.

Earth Dog

Dogs with a balanced "earth" constitution are loyal, friendly, emotionally empathetic, and, at times, seem worried. The Earth Dog's physical characteristics are dense, thick muscles, a broad strong body and a deep chest. This dog may not be quick to learn or fleet of foot, but he shows great endurance and a consistent, steady, and tolerant nature. Earth Dogs generally are good, easy-going, family dogs. They exhibit a calm and grounded demeanor. Maintaining a consistent routine is important to them. Common breeds for Earth Dogs are the Basset Hound, Labrador and Golden Retrievers, Newfoundland, Saint Bernard, and other Giant Breeds.

Though your dog could care less about Traditional Chinese Medicine's conceptual base, we wanted to give you some exposure to it because it offers a fascinating and unending exploration in natural healing. *The Well-Connected Dog: A Guide to Canine Acupressure* is intended to make acupressure accessible to people who want to communicate their caring intention to their dogs.

chapter three

STEP-BY-STEP CANINE ACUPRESSURE TREATMENT

T his is an important moment. It is the moment in the day when you finally can spend some connecting time with your dog, letting all the pressures wash away from you. Touch your dog's head, feel his warmth and responsiveness. Take three deep breaths, look up at the sky, then pick up a dog toy and catch your dog's attention. A few minutes of enjoying and playing with each other is one way to prepare for an acupressure treatment.

The acupressure treatment starts when you and your dog connect. These moments can take many shapes and forms. After play time on the beach with an older dog, whose

achy hips need soothing, is a good time to settle into a treatment. Another good time to start a treatment is when your wonderfully wild and energetic puppy is ready to slow down and snuggle. Some people give their dog a treatment before going to obedience training class.

An acupressure treatment is a dynamic, energetic interaction between two equal partners—you and your dog. Your role is to have the

---

Acupressure Treatment

Pre-Treatment
  Selecting a location
  When not to perform an acupressure treatment
  Preparing yourself
  Introducing yourself and gaining permission to treat
  Observing your dog before treatment

Phases of the Acupressure Treatment
  Observing your dog during treatment
  Phases of an acupressure treatment:
    Opening
    Point work
    Closing
    Stretches.

Post Treatment

---

clear intention to enhance his well-being. To accomplish this, you must be consciously present and use your knowledge, experience, and intuition throughout the treatment process. The other half of the partnership is your dog's innate ability to feel energetic sensations in his body and his capacity to communicate with you through body language.

Once your dog becomes accustomed to having acupressure treatments, he will really think of it as a *treat*! Dogs are very aware of when we are attuned to their needs. In turn, he will help guide you through a treatment—if you are alert to the directions he gives you. Allowing your dog to communicate what he needs is a significant part of sharing an acupressure treatment.

We now will take you through an acupressure treatment step-by-step. A treatment is divided into three parts: before, during, and after. The key to performing a successful acupressure treatment is to pay attention to your dog, with healing intent, while working through each segment of the treatment.

Pre-Treatment

Selecting a Treatment Location

To achieve the best results, select a place where your dog feels safe and relaxed. Most dogs are comfortable in their own living area. If he has a special bed, rug or sunny spot, it is fine to work with him there. For a small dog, a grooming table or couch will

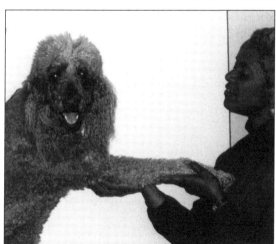

work well. Let your dog choose whether or not he wants to lie down, sit, or stand. Allow him to decide which direction he wants to face during the treatment. There is no need to have a lead. You do not want to restrict your dog's ability to move around during the treatment because he will be giving you cues about how he is feeling.

Make sure you are comfortable, too. You might have to shift your position fairly often during the treatment; it helps prevent stress on

Maya and Marekah Stewart

your muscles and joints. An acupressure treatment needs to be a pleasure for both of you. Consider the possibility of your dog reacting to some of the points that may be tender to the touch. For your own safety, if you know your dog has a tendency to over-react or bite, have someone assist during the treatment.

When there are other dogs in the household, they usually enjoy being in the same environment where energetic work is being done. As pack animals, dogs receive benefit from a treatment by just being in the room. Most often the other dogs will lie down near where you are working and go to sleep, sending calming signals to the dog that is receiving the treatment.

Pick a time of day when your dog has had enough exercise and isn't hungry. The quieter and calmer the environment, the better.

When Not to Perform an Acupressure Treatment

There are times when acupressure treatments are contraindicated. The purpose of an acupressure treatment is to rebalance the body's Chi energy. But there are specific conditions when the body needs to focus energy in a particular way, and interfering with the energy flow could be harmful. During pregnancy, the body's energy is naturally out of balance and needs to stay that way for the duration of the pregnancy. When you have a pregnant female, acupressure treatments are not recommended. In Chapter Seven, Acupressure Treatment for Specific Conditions, particular acupressure points are identified that are not to be used during pregnancy.

When not to perform an acupressure treatment:

- Just after feeding; wait three to four hours before beginning a treatment.
- After a strenuous workout or training session; wait until the dog has cooled down and is calm.
- When your dog has a high fever; call your veterinarian immediately.
- If your dog has an infectious disease; call your veterinarian immediately.
- After a stud has expelled semen; wait twelve hours before a treatment.
- When your bitch is pregnant; resume treatments after delivery.

Preparing Yourself

To achieve the highest quality treatment, you need to feel connected to your own Chi energy and be centered within yourself prior to beginning. Clearing your mind of the day's demands and activities will help you focus your energy and create your healing intent. To clear your mind of distracting thoughts, try the following breathing exercise:

- Sit quietly for several moments and picture your thoughts as clouds floating out of view.
- Breathe in Chi energy from the air and feel it moving through your lungs and down into your abdomen.
- Hold the Chi in your abdomen for several seconds and feel its balancing properties.
- Exhale and follow the vibration of your breath as it moves across the room.
- Repeat this exercise for eight breaths.

After completing the breathing exercise, slowly focus and feel your own energy. Then picture your dog and conceptualize your intent to assist in his healing process. These simple activities will increase your awareness of your own Chi energy, reduce tension in your body, and heighten your ability to *feel* your dog's energy.

Introducing Yourself and Gaining Permission

Dogs appreciate it if you say hello before you begin an acupressure treatment. Take a moment to talk to your dog, while gently touching and stroking him. When you feel connected, ask him, either aloud or to yourself, if you can give him a treatment; then wait for a response. Signs of his acceptance are: turning toward you, softening his eyes, licking your hand, moving his body into yours, or communicating energetically. If you receive no response, ask again. If he does not respond on the second request, move with him to a different location and ask again. If you still receive no response, honor your dog's choice. Having a dog give no response usually means he simply does not want to be treated at that time. Ask again on another day.

Observing Your Dog

Observation is an art. It requires all of your attention and perception. Use all of your senses, intuition, and knowledge of your dog. When observing your dog with this level of intensity, you will be able to develop a baseline of information for treatment. Additionally, you will have information for comparison with subsequent treatments. We suggest that you keep a record of your treatments, noting any changes.

Look at your dog's body objectively, and ask yourself the following questions:

- What is his general demeanor?
- Are his eyes dull or bright?
- Is he over or under weight?
- What is the condition of his coat?
- Is his coat dull, lifeless, dry, or shiny?
- Are there any bare spots on his coat?
- Are there areas he has been scratching?
- What is the condition of his nails?
- Are there any unusual odors?
- Is he alert and listening to you?
- Does he appear to be in pain?
- Are there any signs of recent injury?

Ask the following questions, while watching your dog in motion:

- Are his movements smooth?
- Is his reach even on both the right and left sides?
- Can he switch leads easily?
- Does he show any stiffness in his joints?
- Does he hold his head erect and straight?

Acupressure Treatment

Observing Your Dog During Treatment

Your dog may respond to acupressure in obvious and subtle ways. Obvious reactions could be: muscle spasms, back hollowing, licking, salivating, panting, chewing, or yawning more than usual. Other reactions include: moving away from or into the point of pressure, stretching, a distinct change in his breathing pattern, or scratching or licking himself in a particular area of his body. Record his energetic reactions because they are clues to understanding the rebalancing of energy your dog is experiencing.

Equally important are the more subtle signs your dog may display during a treatment. Note changes in his facial expressions, such as softening of the eyes, or relaxing of the mouth, chin, or ears. Notice any abdominal sounds. Many of these are signs of energy release along a meridian.

As you sharpen your skills of observation, the list of your dog's reactions will expand. Your awareness of the dog's body and its healing process will grow as you pay close attention to all of the changes occurring.

Maintaining a record of your dog's reactions to an acupressure treatment is an important tool for developing your skills of observation. By recording reactions, you have information for future treatments and benchmarks for understanding past behaviors and health conditions. Having a record also is useful when discussing your dog's health with your veterinarian. A detailed outline for a Treatment Log is included in Chapter Six, Acupressure Maintenance Treatment.

Acupressure Treatment Phases

Within the treatment segment of the entire acupressure treatment there are four phases:

> ▸ Opening
> ▸ Point Work
> ▸ Closing
> ▸ Stretches

As you progress through each of these treatment phases, relax and be receptive to the energetic messages your dog is giving you. Remember to clear your mind and center your energy so you can concentrate on your healing intent. Allow your breathing to become deep and relaxed; this will assist in balancing your dog's Chi and will help promote the healing effect.

Set aside enough time for the treatment so you will not feel rushed. As you gain competence, you will be able to complete a treatment in less time. Generally, the duration of a complete treatment is twenty-five minutes to one hour: for the Opening phase, allow approximately 5-10 minutes; for Point Work, 10-30 minutes; for the Closing, 5-10 minutes; and for the Stretches, 5-10 minutes.

Opening

The Opening prepares your dog for bodywork, by enhancing his awareness of his body and allowing him to relax and become comfortable with structured touch.

To Open, position your palm in full contact with your dog's body. Apply about one-half to two pounds of pressure with your palm, with your fingers remaining relaxed. Start on the upper part of your dog's neck. Stroke down along the Bladder Meridian from the neck to the shoulders. The Bladder Meridian runs about one-half to two finger widths, depending on your dog's size, off the spine on either side of his body.

BLADDER MERIDIAN CHART

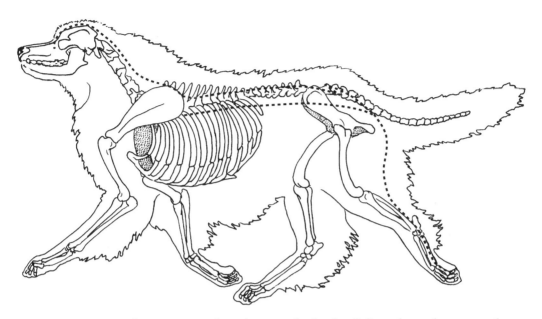

Continue to apply pressure and stroke over the back, gliding along the rump, down the gluteal muscles and hamstrings. Follow the contour of the back of the leg to the hock, and stay lateral from there all the way down to the paw. Repeat this Opening procedure two or three times on both sides of the dog's body. The slow but fluid pace at which you Open expresses your intent in a calming manner.

While performing the Opening, distinguish differences in your dog's body temperature and muscle tone. Notice surface protrusions and depressions. When there is a deficiency, acupressure points along the meridian often feel like soft, spongy depressions. When the Chi energy is excessive, points can feel rigid and resistant to the touch. These findings will help guide you when doing the acupoint work discussed in the next section. Record reactions and observations in your Treatment Log for the Opening phase of the treatment.

Point Work Concepts

Point Work is the second phase of an acupressure treatment and the foundation of the acupressure treatment. The intent of Point Work is to stimulate specific acupoints along a meridian, to balance the dog's energy and promote an environment for healing. By stimulating specific, individual acupoints along a meridian, energy blocks are released. If the Chi energy is excessive, you need to sedate or disperse the energy so the natural flow of Chi resumes. If the Chi is deficient along the meridian, you need to draw more energy to it by tonifying and strengthening the acupressure point in order to resolve the deficiency. When energy is harmoniously balanced, the body's natural ability to heal is restored.

Acupressure points, also called acupoints, have specific qualities and characteristics. They most often are located in valleys of the body, in depressions next to or between muscles and bones, and the areas surrounding joints. See Chapter Five, Canine Acupressure Points, for further information regarding the function and attributes of acupoints.

Selecting the Point Work for an acupressure treatment begins during the Opening segment of a treatment. While performing the Opening, focus on finding areas of energy blockage and observe reactions your dog may have to your touch. A spontaneous pain reaction at any point may indicate an imbalance in that meridian. Tenderness revealed by light pressure indicates there is excessive Chi energy. Tenderness revealed by slightly heavier pressure, or a soft, cool feeling to a point, may indicate an area that is deficient in Chi energy.

Learning the characteristics of acupoints is extremely important. The amount of knowledge needed to have a comprehensive grasp of the concepts related to acupoints and acupressure treatments is beyond the scope of this manual. Many people, not fully versed in all of the depth and complexity of Traditional Chinese Medicine, have applied acupressure treatments and received positive results. The following description of acupoints offers a way to discern some of their attributes.

The *feel*, texture and temperature of an acupoint provides information about that point. Points are considered either in excess or deficient. As your proficiency in feeling energy increases, you will become increasingly aware of the distinctions between the two. Points may exhibit the following attributes:

EXCESS ACUPOINTS	DEFICIENT ACUPOINTS
Protruding	Depressed
Warm	Cool or cold
Painful or Sensitive	Vacant or Empty
Tender to light pressure	Tender to deep pressure
Hard or Dense	Soft or Spongy
Acute	Chronic

Point Work

When an acupoint has an excess of Chi, it may protrude and feel warm to the touch. Often, these points are sensitive to light pressure. Your dog may react by showing signs of discomfort when you touch that point. Excessive points need to be sedated and the energy dispersed. To sedate a point, apply light pressure, feel for a line or place of resistance and stop applying pressure at that level until the resistance dissolves. Then apply slightly more pressure until you again feel some resistance. Wait until the resistance dissolves and exert a little more pressure. The process of sedating a point may take as long as 10-15 minutes, so be patient and proceed slowly.

If the excess point is too tender to work, work the points located in front of it and behind it on the same meridian. This will help balance the energy of the meridian. Once the adjacent points have been sedated, your dog may allow you to work the original excess point.

When a point is deficient in energy, it will often palpate as a depression, be cool or cold, and soft to the touch. The point may be tender to deep pressure. A deficient point usually indicates a chronic condition, as opposed to an acute condition. When a point feels deficient, you need to strengthen or tonify the energy. To tonify a point, apply pressure in short, pulsating thumb movements. Tonifying a point takes less time than sedating a point. A good indication of sufficient stimulation to a deficient point is a warming of that point.

Point Work Techniques

There are three Point Work techniques recommended for canine acupressure:

> ‣ Direct thumb pressure technique
> ‣ Pulsing thumb technique
> ‣ Circular thumb technique.

Experiment with each of the three Point Work techniques. Practice them on a willing friend to become more proficient before working on your dog. The thumb is most commonly selected for Point Work because it is neutral in polarity. By applying neutral polarity to acupoints, you can avoid the possibility of further accentuating an imbalance by the addition of a positive or negative charge.

Synchronize your breathing pattern with the stimulation of points. Breathe out, while easing into the point; breathe in, while slowly releasing the point. After a few treatments, your dog is likely to synchronize his breathing with yours.

Use partial body weight; this ensures a smoothness of motion and protects your thumbs and wrists from stress. Be sure to modify this technique based on the size of your dog. A smaller dog, such as a Yorkshire Terrier or Toy Poodle, requires only ounces of pressure. Large and giant dogs, such as a German Shepherd or Great Pyrenees, requires one-half to three pounds of pressure. Initially, apply light pressure then slowly increase the amount of pressure as your dog permits.

After a few weeks of regular acupressure treatments, most dogs begin to tell you which points need work. Watch your dog's body language; he will tell you the points needing work by touching a point with his nose, by moving his body into a point you are working, or by scratching a particular point. Dogs are highly attuned to body work and quickly understand that we are contributing to their health and well-being. This is a wonderful form of communication and connection you can have with your dog.

General Guidelines For Acupoint Work

▶ Point Work is performed generally from front to rear and top to bottom.

▶ Keep both hands on your dog while giving a treatment. One hand does the Point Work, while the other feels reactions, such as muscle spasms or twitches and releases. The hand not doing Point Work, also serves to soothe your dog and acts as an energy connection.

▶ Breathe out, while moving into a point; breathe in, when letting up on the point.

▶ Use partial body weight; this ensures a smoothness of motion and protects your thumbs and wrists from stress.

▶ Apply pressure gently as you ease into a point and slowly release out of a point. All movements must be smooth and even, no abrupt changes in pressure. Start by applying one-half to two pounds of pressure (take your dog's size into consideration), increasing only as your dog allows.

▶ Apply pressure at a 90-degree angle to the meridian line on which you are working.

Direct Thumb Pressure

To perform Point Work using the direct thumb technique, place the ball of your thumb on the acupressure point perpendicular to its meridian. Gently apply direct pressure, one-half to two pounds (modify pressure in relation to the size of the dog) to the point while breathing out. Slowly release the point while breathing in and move to the next point.

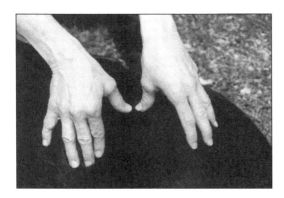

Pulsing Thumb Technique

A light yet firm, slow pulsing thumb motion sedates or disperses excessive Chi energy. A light, fast pulsing motion tonifies or strengthens a deficient area by drawing energy into the point and surrounding area. While using the pulsating thumb technique, strive to maintain rhythmic movements.

Circular Thumb Technique

Begin with the direct thumb pressure technique. After easing into the point, continue to apply pressure while rotating your thumb in a circular motion. Clockwise rotation tonifies or strengthens energy. Counterclockwise motion sedates or disperses energy. Complete three to nine full revolutions before moving to the next point.

Clockwise rotation to tonify or strenghthen acupoint.

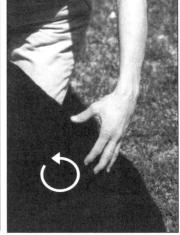

Counter clockwise rotation to sedate, or disperse energy.

Closing

The Closing, phase three of the acupressure treatment, has two purposes: (1) it reinforces the energy flow between the points on the same meridians stimulated during point work; and (2) it establishes a healthy cellular memory pattern.

Reinforcing the energy along the entire meridian system helps maintain the state achieved during Point Work. Cellular memory is the cell's learned response to a chronic stimulus such as pain. The Closing phase eventually replaces the cell's previously learned negative response with a positive response.

There are two basic closing techniques: Smooth Hand, and Cupped Hand. Try each of these and choose the one most comfortable and effective for you and your dog. You also may choose a combination of techniques for your Closing.

Smooth Hand Closing

To perform a Closing using the smooth hand technique, position the palm of your hand in full contact with your dog. Exert light pressure and glide your hand over your dog's body from front to rear, and top to bottom. Begin at the neck over the shoulders, across the back and over the hind quarters. Continue down the back leg, past the hock, and completing the Closing at the end of the dog's paw.

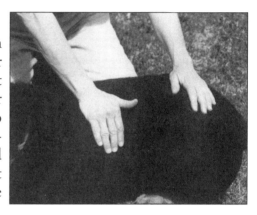

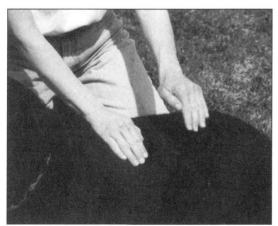

Cupped Hand Closing

To perform the cupped hand Closing, position your hand in a relaxed pyramid shape. A side view of your hand will look like an "A." When you perform this technique, your palm does not make full contact with your dog. Keeping your wrists relaxed assures the effectiveness of this technique. Use your two hands alternately to pat the dog's body in a continuous, rhythmic action. Begin at the top of the neck, moving from front to rear and top to bottom. This Closing technique is best suited for large or giant breeds and provides a stimulating yet relaxing finish to the acupressure treatment.

General Guidelines For Closing

- Closing work is performed from front to rear and top to bottom.

- Keep both hands on your dog while Closing. One hand does the Closing work, the other serves to calm your dog and acts as a connection.

- Movements are smooth and without any abrupt changes in pressure.

- Use your whole body when applying a Closing technique.

- Complete the Closing technique twice, on both sides of your dog, for all of the meridians worked during the treatment.

Stretches

Stretches are the fourth and final segment of an acupressure treatment. They reinforce the treatment by enhancing the energy flow. Their purpose is to increase your dog's overall flexibility and increase the suppleness of the soft tissue, leading to an improved level of performance. Stretches are not only an important part of the acupressure treatment, they also can be a significant part of any exercise or training routine. A complete chapter is devoted to stretches because of their benefit to your dog. Chapter Six, Canine Stretches, provides in-depth stretch instructions.

Post-Treatment

After a complete acupressure treatment, the Chi energy flow in your dog's body is changing, his body awareness has been shifted, and blockages in his meridian pathways have been released. Your dog is experiencing new and different physical sensations. He may be calm and want to rest for a while. Let him have free time to do whatever is comfortable for him. Completion of the rebalancing of energy can take up to 24 hours after an acupressure treatment.

General Post Treatment Guidelines

- After a treatment, your dog may appear "worse" before he feels better. Chi energy flows through the body on a 24-hour cycle, and it can take a complete cycle to experience the benefits of the treatment.

- Check your dog every two to three hours and record in your Treatment Log any changes in behavior, movement, or mannerisms.

- Allow your dog to rest for 24 hours or longer before resuming training or strenuous exercise.

Little Josie: A Story of Survival

Lisa and her husband were taking a vacation in Cozumel, Mexico in an attempt to salvage their marriage. A few days into the vacation, Lisa felt despondent, she realized that nothing could save the relationship. She even considered the desperate act of taking her own life.

That evening, as they drove back to their hotel from a restaurant, Lisa saw a small furry ball spin out and away from under the taxi cab in front of them. Her husband swerved their car to avoid hitting it and then stopped to see what it was.

It was dusk, Lisa looked around but saw nothing, the she heard a faint mean little growl coming from a bush on the side of the road. The headlights of a passing car revealed the tiny face of a scrawny, dirty puppy. Lisa scooped up the puppy in one hand and tucked her into a scarf.

When they got back to the hotel, Lisa spent hours picking fleas, ticks, and tar off of the puppy's skinny, weak, tired body. The next day, Lisa found a veterinarian who, after some cajoling, gave the puppy the shots she needed to be permitted into the United States. Lisa planned to head home the next day. Giving the puppy immunization shots was risky because the puppy's system was already overburdened with trying to survive. Adding the extra chemicals could cause liver failure. Lisa didn't feel she had any good choices. The shots could kill the puppy, yet leaving the puppy in Mexico would mean sure death.

In the midst of this ordeal, Lisa realized she was no longer depressed and thinking about suicide. She was too concerned about the tiny little puppy with a ferocious growl to think about herself and her problem marriage. She had to take care of this little life that literally rolled her way.

By the time Lisa arrived back in the States, the puppy was lethargic and her belly had become severely distended. Lisa rushed to her veterinarian who didn't hold out much hope for the puppy's survival and suggested putting her down. She wasn't ready to end the struggling little puppy's life. So, Lisa called a friend at The Best Friends Sanctuary in Utah to help figure out what to do. The friend suggested contacting Equine and Canine Acupressure since they were just a few miles away from Lisa's house. After a

Josie and her adopted raccoon family

quick call, Lisa drove as fast as she could to Elbert County, Colorado with the puppy on her lap.

Nancy Zidonis and Marie Soderberg assessed the puppy's critical condition and performed an acupressure treatment involving Point Work on the following meridians: Liver, Kidney, Spleen Bladder and Conception and Governing Vessels. After the first acupressure treatment and selected homeopathy, the puppy, who still had no name, showed quite a bit of improvement. Her belly was not as bloated; she was able to walk around, drink water and eat a little. This was the beginning of her road back to complete health.

After a few weeks of treatments, it was obvious that Nancy had become deeply bonded with the puppy, now named Josephine. Lisa kindly gave "Josie" to Nancy for safekeeping, knowing she could spend as much time as she wanted with her furry treasure from Mexico.

chapter four

CANINE
MERIDIAN SYSTEM

Understanding how the meridian system works will help you when performing an acupressure treatment on your dog. We invite you to read this chapter to your dog to show him how much you love him and all you are doing for him. His tail will wag as you read. Don't be surprised if he feels so good that he needs to take a nap.

Meridians

Meridians are the pathways that carry Chi energy throughout the body. In Chinese theory, these pathways are invisible yet very real. Chi moves through the meridians, transporting nourishment, strength and healing properties. The meridian system connects and unifies the entire body, linking internal organs and external body. In TCM, we constantly strive to maintain a naturally balanced state within the meridian system. When the meridians are balanced and the Chi is flowing smoothly, health and self-healing exist.

Since the Chi circulates through the meridian system and connects the interior with the exterior of the dog's body, we can influence the flow of Chi by touching various points, known as acupressure points, or acupoints, along a meridian.

In both humans and dogs, the meridian system consists of twelve bilateral major meridians. Each of these meridians is associated with a specific organ system. In addition to the twelve major meridians, there are eight, non-paired, Extraordinary Vessels. The eight Extraordinary Vessels do not have an organ system directly associated with them. Two of these— the Governing Vessel and the Conception Vessel—are considered part of the major meridian system partially because they have acupressure points that are not on any other meridian.

Outside of a dog, a book is man's best friend. Inside a dog, it's too dark to read.— Groucho Marx

Meridian Imbalance

Meridian theory is based on the belief that when there is a blockage, or some form of interruption along a meridian pathway where the Chi does not flow smoothly, it will cause an imbalance or disharmony. An imbalance can cause a local dysfunction and

The exact locations of canine and human meridians vary, depending on the source. It is difficult to identify a "right" location. Meridian drawings are a guide, not an exact road map.

Learning to feel the energy along the meridians will help develop your "energy awareness." Begin by tracing the meridian lines on your dog, using the charts as a guide. Trace each meridian several times until you feel the energy-flow pattern, while your dog enjoys this new sensory experience.

eventually a disease in the organ associated with the meridian. For example, a disharmony in the Small Intestine Meridian may manifest as a shoulder ache because the Small Intestine Meridian passes through the shoulder. Another example: A disharmony in the Gall Bladder Meridian may appear as a sciatic problem since the Gall Bladder Meridian travels through the hip and down the back leg. If imbalances are left untreated, physical discomfort becomes more severe and disease manifests.

In TCM an imbalance in a meridian is either a condition of excess or deficient Chi. Blocked, congested, or stagnated Chi is caused by external and internal influences. An external influence would be a cold, damp wind; while an internal influence may be extreme anger. Once a disharmony in the meridian system occurs, the TCM practitioner uses many indicators to assess the animal's condition to understand the cause of the disharmony before arriving at a course of treatment.

Meridian Organ Systems

An organ system is responsible for its specific associated organ as well as for the impact the organ has on the entire body. Each organ system governs a particular part of the body, soft tissues, emotions, and functions. Another name for the organ system is *Zang-Fu* Organs. The Zang Organs are Yin Organs that tend to be dense and are responsible for storing and transforming body substances. The Fu Organs are Yang and tend to be hollow and transport nutrients and body waste. The Zang-Fu Organs function to maintain the harmonious flow of Chi energy through the meridians.

ZANG / YIN	FU / YANG
Lung	Large Intestine
Kidney	Bladder
Liver	Gall Bladder
Heart	Small Intestine
Pericardium	Triple Warmer
Spleen	Stomach

Zang-Fu Organs are paired as sister meridians. One of the pair is Yin, the other is Yang. The Zang/Yin sister meridians flow along the underside, or ventral aspect, of the dog's body while the Fu/Yang sister meridians travel along the top, or dorsal aspect, of the dog's body. Lung and Large Intestine are sister meridians. The Lung Meridian is the Zang/Yin meridian and the Large Intestine is the Fu/Yang meridian. Often, sister meridians are worked on during the same acupressure treatment, because one is the reflection of the other. If one sister meridian has an excess of Chi, the other will have a deficiency of Chi. Working with one or both of the sister meridians can resolve an imbalance.

Chi Energy along the Meridians

Chi circulates through the meridian system once every 24 hours. Chi energy is concentrated for approximately two hours in each of the twelve major meridians. During these periods of energy concentration, stimulating the acupressure points along the meridian associated with the time period will produce more powerful

DIRECTION AND TIME FLOW
OF CHI ENERGY ALONG MERIDIANS

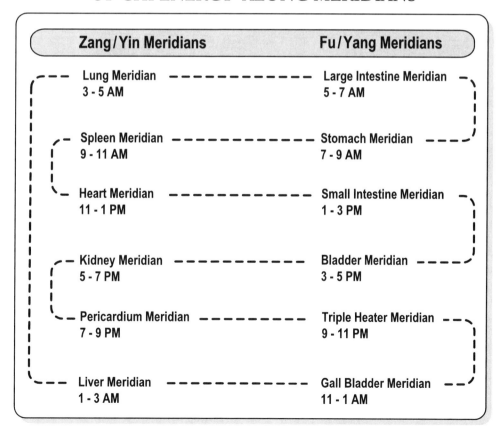

Zang/Yin Meridians	Fu/Yang Meridians
Lung Meridian 3 - 5 AM	Large Intestine Meridian 5 - 7 AM
Spleen Meridian 9 - 11 AM	Stomach Meridian 7 - 9 AM
Heart Meridian 11 - 1 PM	Small Intestine Meridian 1 - 3 PM
Kidney Meridian 5 - 7 PM	Bladder Meridian 3 - 5 PM
Pericardium Meridian 7 - 9 PM	Triple Heater Meridian 9 - 11 PM
Liver Meridian 1 - 3 AM	Gall Bladder Meridian 11 - 1 AM

results. For instance, if there is a condition that indicates a Kidney imbalance, working acupressure points along the Kidney Meridian will have a stronger effect between five and seven P.M.

Learning the Meridians

The best way to learn the location of each of the twelve meridians and the two Extraordinary Vessels is to take a half an hour daily for a week to trace them on your dog. Find a location where you and your dog are comfortable and safe: either on a soft grassy area, carpeted floor, or place your dog on a table. Make sure you do not strain any part of your body while working on your dog. Place your palm down on the dog. Lightly stroke your dog, tracing the line of each meridian. The more familiar you are with the meridian pathways, the more readily you will understand and perform an acupressure treatment. This also is a good way to prepare your dog for the new sensory experiences of an acupressure treatment.

I lie belly up
In the sunshine, happier than
You ever will be.

Dog Haiku, email

OBSERVATIONS

Look at your dog's body objectively, and ask yourself the following questions:

What is his general demeanor _____

_____

Are his eyes dull or bright? _____

_____

Is he over or under weight _____

_____

What is the condition of his coat? _____

_____

Is his coat dull, lifeless, dry or shiny? _____

_____

Are there any bare spots on his coat? _____

_____

Are there areas he has been scratching? _____

_____

What is the condition of his nails? _____

_____

Are there any unusual odors? _____

_____

Is he alert and listening to you? _____

Does he appear to be in pain? _____

Are there any signs of recent injury? _____

_____

Ask the following questions, while watching your dog in motion:

Are his movements smooth? _____

_____

Is his reach even on both the right and left sides? _____

_____

Can he switch leads easily? _____

_____

Does he show any stiffness in his joints? _____

_____

Does he hold his head erect and straight? _____

_____

LUNG MERIDIAN
controller of receiving chi

SISTER MERIDIAN - Large Intestine
MAXIMAL TIME - 3 - 5 am
ENERGY - YIN
ELEMENT - Metal

SEASON - Fall
GOVERNED PART OF BODY -
   Skin and Body Hair
COLOR - White or Silver

INDICATORS

PHYSICAL

Respiratory conditions including asthma,
   pneumonia or coughing
Chest pain or congestion
Dry skin or dull coat

BEHAVIOR

Compulsive behaviors
Chronic grief
Depression

FUNCTION

The Lung Meridian takes in Chi from the air and builds resistance to external intrusions. It regulates the secretion of sweat and skin moistening. It also regulates body hair and skin. This meridian eliminates noxious gases through exhalation.

It is said that the Lung Meridian rules the Chi. The lungs receive Chi, change it and disburse it throughout the entire body. How much or how little Chi is absorbed defines the Chi. Shallow breaths display as erratic and often nervous energy. Deep breaths create more vitality and grounding. Since air has Chi, as the dog inhales, Chi is brought into his lungs. The outer air Chi in the lungs blends with the Chi from the digestive system and forms what is known as "Gathering Chi." The Gathering Chi is the life force energy that maintains the animal and its physiological activities. The Lungs then distribute this essential life force energy throughout the body.

LOCATION

The Lung Meridian begins internally and surfaces in the hollow of the chest, where it meets the inside of the foreleg, near the underarm in the pectoral muscle. This point is known as Lu 1. The meridian then flows upward at a slight angle, then down to the forearm and runs along the inside edge of the large muscle on the forearm. Then, it flows on the inside edge of the lower leg, ending at the tip of the dewclaw. There are 11 acupoints on the Lung Meridian.

LUNG MERIDIAN

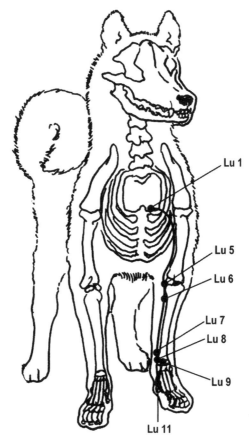

Lu 1

Lu 5

Lu 6

Lu 7

Lu 8

Lu 9

Lu 11

POINT	TYPE OF POINT *Traditional Name*	FUNCTION
Lu 1	Alarm Point for the lung *Central Palace*	Relieves fatigue and strengthens the lungs. Use for loud coughs or asthma.
Lu 5	Sedation Point *Foot Marsh*	Main point for muscular disorders and foreleg pain. Relieves elbow pain.
Lu 7	Connecting Point *Broken Sequence*	Master Point for the head and neck. Use for any respiratory condition.
Lu 9	Tonification and Source Point *Great Abyss*	Influential Points for arteries. Relieves breathing difficulties and clears the lungs. Relieves elbow and shoulder pain.
Lu 11	Ting Point *Lesser Metal*	Use for acute emergencies such as respiratory failure or collapse. Strengthens the immune system.

LARGE INTESTINE MERIDIAN
the great eliminator

SISTER MERIDIAN - Lung
MAXIMAL TIME - 5 - 7 am
ENERGY - Yang
ELEMENT - Metal

SEASON - Fall
GOVERNED PART OF BODY -
  Skin and Body Hair
COLOR - White or Silver

INDICATORS

PHYSICAL

Constipation or diarrhea
Respiratory conditions
Restricted or tight muscles of the neck
Skin problems
Weak immune system

BEHAVIOR

Excessive apprehension
Stubbornness

FUNCTION

The large intestine receives food and water from the small intestine, then absorbs some of the fluids and excretes the remainder. The elimination function of the large intestine has an energetic as well as a physical importance. This meridian helps remove stagnant Chi energy through excretion. Additionally, the Large Intestine Meridian supports the lung in its functions of respiration and immune system activities.

LOCATION

The Large Intestine Meridian begins at the front inside corner of the foreleg on the medial side of the second toe. From here the meridian flows up on the inside middle of the foreleg. It then crosses laterally over the wrist and flows up, on the topside of the foreleg, to the elbow, up the shoulder and across the ventral portion of the neck. It crosses the mandible and ends at the bottom of the nostril. There are 20 acupoints along this meridian.

LARGE INTESTINE MERIDIAN

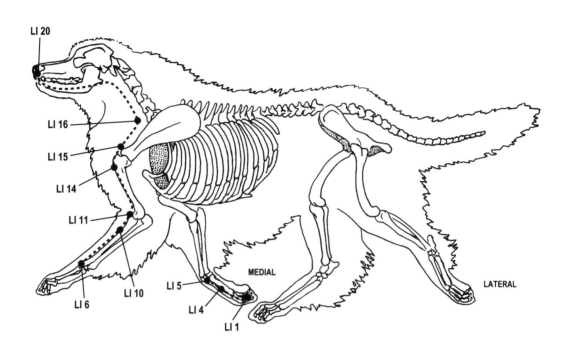

POINT	TYPE OF POINT *Traditional Name*	FUNCTION
LI 4	Source Point *Joining Valley*	Master Point for the face and mouth. Relieves head, neck, foreleg and shoulder pain. Important pain reducing point, beneficial for pain in any part of the body. Balances the gastrointestinal system. Builds the immune system. Use in conjunction with LI 11.
LI 6	*Slanting Passage*	Connecting Point to the Lung meridian. Relieves throat problems and pain in the foreleg.
LI 10	*Arm Three Miles*	Use to relieve pain or paralysis of the arm or shoulder. Helps arthritic conditions of the elbow. Builds endurance. Important tonification point.
LI 11	Tonification Point *Crooked Pond*	Relieves diarrhea and benefits the immune system. Use for arthritic elbow, acute lower back pain and in the treatment of allergic and infectious disorders.
LI 14	*Upper Arm*	Relieves shoulder tension and relaxes shoulder muscles. Use for relief of stiff neck.
LI 15	*Shoulder Bone*	Relieves arthritis of the elbow and shoulder.

STOMACH MERIDIAN
sea of nourishment

SISTER MERIDIAN - Spleen
MAXIMAL TIME - 7 - 9 am
ENERGY - Yang
ELEMENT - Earth

SEASON - Late Summer
GOVERNED PART OF BODY -
 Muscles & Lymph
COLOR - Yellow

INDICATORS

PHYSICAL

Digestive tract disorders
Eye problems
Stifle problems including
inflammation, pain and arthritis
Jaw tension and pain
Lethargy and weakness

BEHAVIOR

Chronic nervous tension
Anxiety

FUNCTION

The stomach is in charge of digestion. It receives and transforms all food going through the body and assists with its appetite mechanism. The stomach and spleen transport the food essences and Chi to all parts of the body. Stomach Chi and Spleen Chi are responsible for nourishing the muscles. No matter what the disease, it is believed that if the stomach Chi is strong, the outlook is good. Conversely, if the stomach Chi is low, the prognosis is not good.

LOCATION

The Stomach Meridian starts under the eye. This point is St 1. It descends to the nose and travels along the side of the jawbone up to the ear. From here the meridian runs down below the cervical vertebrae, through the chest and along the lower edge of the abdomen and loin regions. It then passes over the front aspect of the thigh and stifle, over the tibia and ends at the edge of the third toe. The Stomach Meridian has 45 acupoints.

STOMACH MERIDIAN

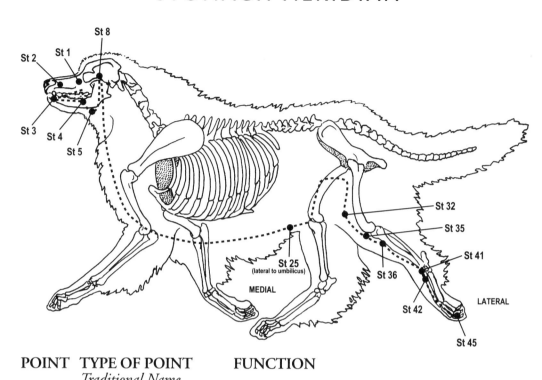

POINT	TYPE OF POINT *Traditional Name*	FUNCTION
St 1	*Receiving Tears*	Use for disorders of the face including eye problems, toothaches, jaw tension and facial paralysis.
St 2	*Four Whites*	Relaxes muscles, tendons and the body in general. Excellent pain relief point.
St 25	Alarm Point for large intestine *Heavenly Pillar*	Use for abdominal disorders and to increase circulation in the legs. Relieves leg pain. Helps relieve diarrhea or constipation and vomiting.
St 35	*Calf's Nose*	Relieves hind leg joint pain. Reduces pain or arthritis of the stifle.
St 36	*Leg Three Miles*	Master Point for the abdomen and gastrointestinal tract. Relieves fatigue. Stimulation of this point benefits digestion and helps restore the immune system. It can be used to increase contractions during labor.
St 41	Tonification Point *Dispersing Stream*	For lameness of the hind legs, hind limb and joint soreness or abdominal disorders.
St 45	Sedation & Ting Point *Evil's Dissipation*	Relieves indigestion and abdominal pain.

SPLEEN MERIDIAN
controller of distribution

SISTER MERIDIAN - Stomach
MAXIMAL TIME - 9 - 11 am
ENERGY - Yin
ELEMENT - Earth

SEASON - Late Summer
GOVERNED PART OF BODY -
 Muscles & Lymph
COLOR - Yellow

INDICATORS

PHYSICAL

Immune system deficiency or disorders
Muscle problems including atrophy
 lack of tone or strength
Digestive disorders including diarrhea
 and weight problems

BEHAVIOR

Timid
Lack of awareness

FUNCTION

The spleen and the stomach assist the digestive processes by transporting and trans-forming food by absorbing the nourishment and then by separating the useable from the unusable food. The spleen is the primary organ in the production of prenatal Chi. Ingested food and drink provide Food Chi, and is the basis for the creation of Postnatal Chi. The spleen governs blood. The Spleen Meridian supplies the essential body energy for the dog and is the core of the immune system.

The Spleen Meridian also governs the muscles, connective tissue and the four limbs; it both originates and carries Chi to these areas. Proper movement is dependent upon a well-balanced Spleen Meridian.

LOCATION

The Spleen Meridian begins on the inside of the hind leg at a point just inside the second toe. It then proceeds up the inner back side of the lower leg, turns slightly forward passing over the inside front of the hock, then up the middle of the inside leg along the back of the tibia to the stifle. It continues to a point halfway up the femur. The Spleen Meridian then slants toward the head, running along the underside of the abdomen. It then turns and travels toward the rear of the dog, ending about in the sixth intercostal space, approximately level with the point of the shoulder.

SPLEEN MERIDIAN

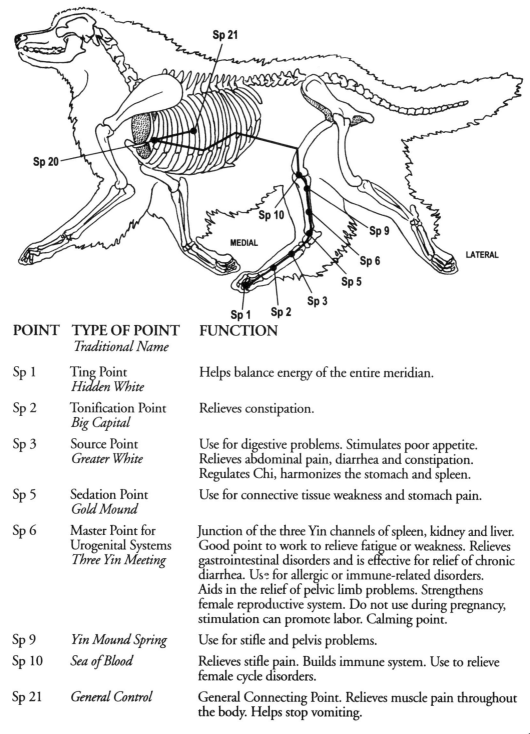

POINT	TYPE OF POINT *Traditional Name*	FUNCTION
Sp 1	Ting Point *Hidden White*	Helps balance energy of the entire meridian.
Sp 2	Tonification Point *Big Capital*	Relieves constipation.
Sp 3	Source Point *Greater White*	Use for digestive problems. Stimulates poor appetite. Relieves abdominal pain, diarrhea and constipation. Regulates Chi, harmonizes the stomach and spleen.
Sp 5	Sedation Point *Gold Mound*	Use for connective tissue weakness and stomach pain.
Sp 6	Master Point for Urogenital Systems *Three Yin Meeting*	Junction of the three Yin channels of spleen, kidney and liver. Good point to work to relieve fatigue or weakness. Relieves gastrointestinal disorders and is effective for relief of chronic diarrhea. Use for allergic or immune-related disorders. Aids in the relief of pelvic limb problems. Strengthens female reproductive system. Do not use during pregnancy, stimulation can promote labor. Calming point.
Sp 9	*Yin Mound Spring*	Use for stifle and pelvis problems.
Sp 10	*Sea of Blood*	Relieves stifle pain. Builds immune system. Use to relieve female cycle disorders.
Sp 21	*General Control*	General Connecting Point. Relieves muscle pain throughout the body. Helps stop vomiting.

HEART MERIDIAN
home of the spirit

SISTER MERIDIAN - Small Intestine
MAXIMAL TIME - 11 am - 1 pm
ENERGY - Yin
ELEMENT - Fire

SEASON - Summer
GOVERNED PART OF BODY -
   Vascular System
COLOR - Red

INDICATORS

PHYSICAL

Shoulder problems
Restlessness, disturbed sleep
Cardiovascular problems including
heart irregularities, shortness of breath
and poor circulation
Nervous system disorders

BEHAVIOR

Hyperactive
Depression

FUNCTION

The Heart Meridian governs the entire vascular system controlling the direction and strength of blood flow. It is the center of emotional and mental consciousness and regulates memory and other brain functions. The Heart Meridian encourages good circulation. Good circulation brings nourishment to the tissues, removes toxins and influences all the other organs. Since it rules the mental energy, it is known as Shen, or spirit of an animal. Because of its importance, the heart has a protector, the pericardium. The Pericardium Meridian helps absorb emotional and physical affronts to the dog.

LOCATION

The Heart Meridian begins close to the heart in the armpit. It travels down the foreleg on the inside, crossing behind the wrist and continuing down the back edge on the outside of the foreleg. It ends at a point on the inside tip of the fifth toe. This is the Ting Point, called Ht 9. There are 9 acupoints along the Heart Meridian.

HEART MERIDIAN

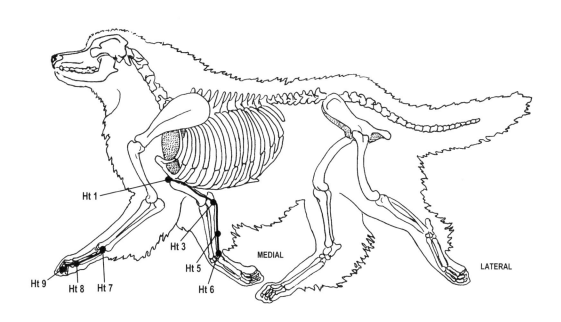

POINT	TYPE OF POINT *Traditional Name*	FUNCTION
Ht 1	*Supreme Spring*	Clears energy flow of the meridian. Relieves arthritis of the shoulder and is useful in relaxing your dog. Relieves depression.
Ht 5	Connecting Point *Inner Communication*	Use to relieve vision disorders. Calms the spirit.
Ht 6	Accumulation Point *Yin Accumulation*	Use for behavioral problems, helps to calm your dog.
Ht 7	Sedation and Source Point *Mind Door*	Use to calm your dog and to relieve confusion.
Ht 9	Ting and Tonification Point *Lesser Yin Rushing*	Helps to balance energy of the entire meridian. Use to reduce fever and for cardiovascular emergencies.

SMALL INTESTINE MERIDIAN
controller of assimilation

SISTER MERIDIAN - Heart
MAXIMAL TIME - 1 - 3 pm
ENERGY - Yang
ELEMENT - Fire

SEASON - Summer
GOVERNED PART OF BODY
   Vascular System
COLOR - Red

INDICATORS

PHYSICAL

Shoulder problems including muscle
 atrophy, lameness or stiffness
Foreleg problems
Neck stiffness
Jaw tension or pain

BEHAVIOR

Lack of mental clarity
Lack of enthusiasm
Depression

FUNCTION

The Small Intestine Meridian has a vital function in the nourishment of the body. It is responsible for receiving and transforming nourishment by absorbing food and drink, separating the pure or useful substances from the impure or waste products. It is also in charge of assimilation of nutrients. On an emotional level, the small intestine rules discernment. It is paired with the Heart Meridian and helps bring clarity of mind.

LOCATION

The Small Intestine Meridian begins on the fifth toe. Staying on the outside of the leg it travels up, over the metacarpal bones, and reaches back slightly as it goes over the elbow. It flows over the triceps muscle to a point right behind the shoulder joint. From here the meridian flows up the scapula, crossing slightly below its top border and continues up the middle of the neck. It touches the jaw bone and ends at a point on the outside of the base of the ear. There are 19 acupoints along the Small Intestine Meridian.

SMALL INTESTINE MERIDIAN

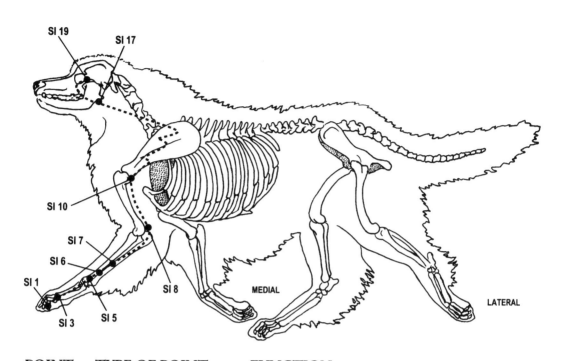

SI 19
SI 17
SI 10
SI 7
SI 6
SI 1
SI 3
SI 5
SI 8
MEDIAL
LATERAL

POINT	TYPE OF POINT *Traditional Name*	FUNCTION
SI 1	Ting Point *Lesser Marsh*	Balances energy of the entire meridian.
SI 3	Tonification Point *Back Stream*	Use for arthritis of the ankle, wrist or shoulder pain. Strengthens the spine. Clears the mind.
SI 5	*Yang Valley*	For muscle spasms of the neck and carpal joint problems. Clears the mind.
SI 6	Accumulation Point *Supporting the Old*	Relieves stiff neck, foreleg and shoulder pain. Benefits the tendons and helps the eyes.
SI 7	Connecting Point *Branch to Heart*	For shoulder, elbow or foreleg problems. Calms the mind.
SI 8	Sedation Point *Small Intestine Sea*	Relieves shoulder, foreleg and elbow pain. Calms the mind.
SI 10	*Scapula's Hollow*	Shoulder release point.
SI 17	*Heaven Appearance*	Softens hard muscles and balances the glands.
SI 19	*Listening Palace*	Benefits the ears.

BLADDER MERIDIAN
the great mediator

SISTER MERIDIAN - Kidney
MAXIMAL TIME - 3 - 5 pm
ENERGY - Yang
ELEMENT - Water

SEASON - Winter
BODY PARTS - Bone & Marrow
COLOR - Blue

INDICATORS

PHYSICAL

Urinary tract problems
Lower back and hock problems
General body pain, muscle spasms
or cramps of the hindquarters
Arthritis, bone or joint problems
Sensitivity in any of the Association Points

BEHAVIOR

Fear
Chronic anxiety
Agitation

FUNCTION

The bladder transforms fluids through storage and excretion. The Bladder Meridian has the unique facility of helping balance the entire meridian system. Association Points along the Bladder Meridian correspond directly with each of the twelve major meridians. If an Association Point is reactive or tender to the touch, it may indicate an energy imbalance in the corresponding meridian. On an emotional level the Bladder Meridian addresses fear, depression, and agitation.

LOCATION

The Bladder Meridian begins on a point at the inside corner of the dog's eye and runs up and over the top of the head. It flows down the neck and at the shoulders it splits into two branches. The two branches follow lines parallel to the spine. The top channel runs 1/2 to 1 1/2 finger widths off the spine, the second branch runs 1 - 3 finger widths lower. The channels flow down the back toward the tail and continue down the hind leg. The two channels pass between the crease of the biceps femoris and semitendinosus muscles. The Bladder Meridian then flows down the outside aspect of the hind leg and ends at Bl 67, the Ting Point. This point is on the lateral aspect of the fifth toe. There are 67 acupoints along the Bladder Meridian.

BLADDER MERIDIAN

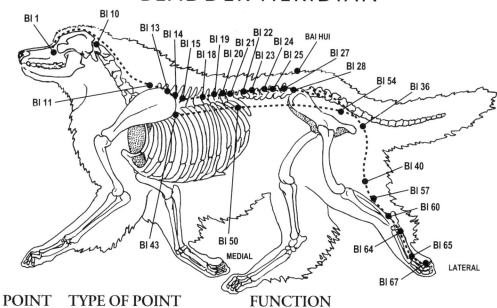

POINT	TYPE OF POINT *Traditional Name*	FUNCTION
Bl 10	*Heaven Pillar*	Cervical, shoulder or back pain.
Bl 11	Influential Point for bone *Big Reed*	Use this point for any type of bone or joint disorder. Helps relieve rheumatoid arthritis. Enhances bone healing.
Bl 13	Lung Association Point	Use for lung problems including bronchitis or asthma.
Bl 14	Pericardium Association Point *Terminal Yin Back*	Calming effect. Regulates the heart.
Bl 15	Heart Association Point	Calming effect. Stimulates the brain
Bl 18	Liver Association Point	Use for liver disorders.
Bl 19	Gall Bladder Association Point	Use for liver and gall bladder disorders. Benefits intervertebral issues.
Bl 20	Spleen Association Point	For calming digestive disorders. Use for medial stifle problems. Reinforce in all chronic conditions.
Bl 21	Stomach Association Point	Use for gastrointestinal disorders and lateral stifle problems.
Bl 22	Triple Heater Association Point	Relieves abdominal pain, hormone problems and lower back pain.
Bl 23	Kidney Association Point	General arthritis point. Helps relieve chronic lower back and lumbosacral pain. Strengthens immune system.
Bl 24	*Sea of Chi*	Relieves lumbosacral pain and moves stagnant Chi.
Bl 25	Large Intestine Association Point	Helps relieve constipation and diarrhea. Relieves pain in the neck, shoulder and lower back. Use for hock and stifle arthritis.
Bl 27	Small Intestine Association Point	Relieves indigestion. Use for sciatica and lower back pain.
Bl 28	Bladder Association Point	Helps relieve urinary bladder problems. Use for neck and back pain.
Bl 40	Master Point for lower back and hips *Supporting Middle*	For arthritis in stifle, hip and lower back.
Bl 60	*Kunlun Mountain*	Aspirin Point. Use for arthritis of the hock and soft tissue injury. Strengthens and releases the back and shoulders.
BL 64	Source Point *Capital Bone*	Relieves neck stiffness and back pain.
Bl 67	Ting and Tonification Point *Reaching Yin*	Balances energy of entire Bladder Meridian.

KIDNEY MERIDIAN
residence of resolution

SISTER MERIDIAN - Bladder
MAXIMAL TIME - 5 - 7 pm
ENERGY - Yin
ELEMENT - Water

SEASON - Winter
GOVERNED PART OF BODY -
   Bone & Marrow
COLOR - Blue

INDICATORS

PHYSICAL

Bone problems including fractures
Periodontal diseases
Dull and lifeless coat
Irregular estrous cycles, fertility problems

BEHAVIOR

Fear or timidity
Chronic anxiety
Poor concentration
Aggression

FUNCTION

The Kidney Meridian houses the "Jing" essence, the substance that underlies all organic life. Jing can be likened to a reservoir of energy that nourishes each cell of the body, fuels the metabolism and maintains the vitality, well-being and function of every system. Although Jing is primarily inherited, it can be supplemented and enhanced by a healthy lifestyle including good nutrition, exercise and energy healing work.

The Kidney Meridian controls the growth and healing of bones. Teeth, which are considered to be a surplus of bone, are also governed by the Kidney Meridian. Since this meridian opens into the ears, proper functioning of the ears depends on a balanced Kidney Meridian. This meridian is responsible for the harmonized sexual functions of your dog.

Emotionally, the Kidney Meridian deals with survival and instinctual fear. A dog who exhibits unusual fear reactions, lacks confidence, or is aggressive will benefit from acupressure work along the Kidney Meridian.

LOCATION

The Kidney Meridian starts at a soft point just under the main foot pad of the hind paw. The meridian travels up the inside of the hind leg to the hock, circles in a clockwise direction, continuing its flow up the inside of the leg to the groin area. It flows along the ventral abdomen, about 2-3 inches off the midline and through the chest, ending at Ki 27, which is located between the breastbone and first rib.

KIDNEY MERIDIAN

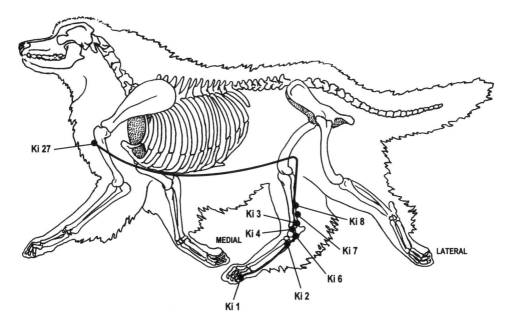

NOTE: Ki 1 is located under main pad of paw

POINT	TYPE OF POINT *Traditional Name*	FUNCTION
Ki 1	Sedation Point *Bubbling Spring*	Use for shock and acute seizure episodes. Emergency point, stimulate vigorously. Use primarily for emergency situations.
Ki 3	Source Point *Greater Stream*	Helps restore the immune system. Estrous cycle irregularity. Use for arthritic hocks. Strengthens the lumbar spine.
Ki 6	*Shining Sea*	Regulates hormones. Releases the shoulders and neck. Calms the spirit, benefits the throat.
Ki 7	Tonification Point *Returning Current*	Stimulate if your dog is fatigued. Aids in relief of hock and back pain.
Ki 8	*Junction of Faithfulness*	Relieves lower back pain and soreness. Builds confidence.
Ki 27	Association Point for all Association Points *Transporting Point Mansion*	Use for respiratory ailments or chest pain.

PERICARDIUM MERIDIAN
heart protector

SISTER MERIDIAN - Triple Heater
MAXIMAL TIME - 7 - 9 pm
ENERGY - Yin
ELEMENT - Fire

SEASON - Summer
GOVERNED PART OF BODY -
  Vascular System
COLOR - Red

INDICATORS

PHYSICAL

Stiffness of the neck, foreleg and elbow
Chest conditions including pneumonia
Irregular heart rhythm including
abnormally rapid heartbeat, heart murmurs

BEHAVIOR

Timid behavior
Depression

FUNCTION

The Pericardium Meridian's main function is to protect the heart from external stresses. This protection manifests on both physical and emotional levels. The Pericardium Meridian supports the heart in circulatory functions. Physically this meridian protects the heart by absorbing heat. Emotionally its purpose is to bring joy and protect the heart from emotional stress. The pericardium accomplishes this by balancing the emotions and calming the heart.

LOCATION

The Pericardium Meridian begins deep within the body at the sac that surrounds the heart. The meridian surfaces in the space between the 5th and 6th ribs, near the elbow. From here it travels down the middle of the inside of the foreleg toward the back side of the wrist. Then it runs down the back inside of the lower leg and ends at the tip of the third toe, Pe 9, the Ting Point. There are 9 acupoints along the Pericardium Meridian.

PERICARDIUM MERIDIAN

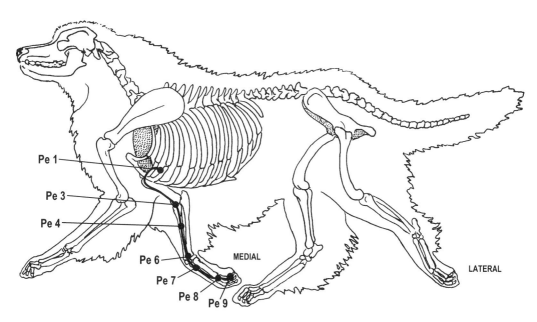

POINT	TYPE OF POINT *Traditional Name*	FUNCTION
Pe 1	*Heavenly Pond*	Use to calm heart palpitations and heart murmurs. Helps with respiratory problems.
Pe 4	*Cleft Door*	Accumulation Point. Calms the heart and relieves fear.
Pe 6	Connecting Point *Inner Gate*	Master Point for chest and cranial abdomen (front of abdomen). Powerful point for all chest conditions including pneumonia. Improves circulation. Powerful anxiety reducer. Balances the internal organs.
Pe 7	Sedation & Source Point *Great Hill*	Local point for wrist. Calms the spirit and regulates the heart.
Pe 9	Ting Point & Tonification Point *Center Rush*	Balances energy of entire meridian. Use also for foreleg arthritis.

TRIPLE HEATER MERIDIAN
commander of all energies

SISTER MERIDIAN - Pericardium
MAXIMAL TIME - 9 - 11 pm
ENERGY - Yang
ELEMENT - Fire

SEASON - Summer
GOVERNED PART OF BODY -
   Vascular System
COLOR - Red

INDICATORS

PHYSICAL

Ear problems

Neck stiffness, tension or pain

Foreleg, shoulder and elbow problems

BEHAVIOR

None

FUNCTION

The Triple Heater is a function rather than a physical organ. It represents a group of energies and involves many organs. This meridian is the functional relationship between the energy-transforming organs. The Triple Heater transforms and transports Chi as it flows unimpeded to all parts of the body. In this role, it helps to excrete waste as well as direct Chi to the organs. This meridian also enhances the function of the lymphatic system.

LOCATION

The Triple Heater Meridian starts at a point on the lateral border of the fourth toe. It flows up the metacarpals and continues up the outside of the upper foreleg. The meridian travels to the elbow, then along the back side of the humerus to the shoulder joint. From here it crosses the scapula and continues up the neck, below the vertebrae, to the ear and ends on the outside border of the eye. There are 23 acupoints along the Triple Heater Meridian.

TRIPLE HEATER MERIDIAN

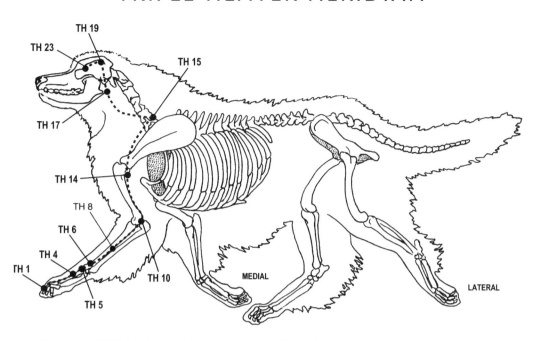

POINT	TYPE OF POINT *Traditional Name*	FUNCTION
TH 4	Source Point *Yang's Pond*	Relieves discomfort such as tendinitis, rheumatism, foreleg edema and arthritis. Relaxes the tendons. Use in chronic disease conditions when energy of the kidneys is deficient.
TH 5	Connecting Point *Outer Gate*	For rheumatic conditions. Helps ease tendinitis. Helps build the immune system. Relieves ear problems.
TH 6	*Branching Ditch*	Use for neck soreness or pain.
TH 8	*Connecting 3 Yang*	Connecting point of three Yang meridians. This is a shoulder, neck and foreleg release point.
TH 10	Sedation Point *Heavenly Well*	For elbow and forelimb soreness, sprains and rheumatic pain. Relaxes tendons.
TH 14	*Shoulder Crevice*	For shoulder lameness or soreness.
TH 17	*Wind Screen*	Use for ear problems.
TH 23	*Silk Bamboo Hole*	Benefits the eyes, relieves pain.

GALL BLADDER MERIDIAN
official of decision and judgment

SISTER MERIDIAN - Liver
MAXIMAL TIME - 11 pm - 1 am
ENERGY - Yang
ELEMENT - Wood

SEASON - Spring
GOVERNED PART OF BODY -
   Ligaments, Tendons
   and Muscles
COLOR - Green

INDICATORS

PHYSICAL

Arthritis-joint stiffness or pain
Hock problems
Muscle stiffness, soreness
Ear and eye problems

BEHAVIOR

Anger or aggression
Depression
Timidity and indecision

FUNCTION

The Gall Bladder Meridian impacts certain aspects of the emotional and energetic properties of your dog. It regulates the flow of Chi throughout the body and governs the decision-making process. Excessive gall bladder Chi may be exhibited as anger, whereas timidity or depression may be a result of insufficient gall bladder Chi. Also, the Gall Bladder Meridian rules many parts of your dog's body including the eyes, ligaments, muscles, tendons and joints.

LOCATION

The Gall Bladder Meridian begins at the outer corner of the eye. It flows to the outer side of the ear, crossing back and forth on the side of the head. It curves behind the ear and flows down the neck to the middle of the scapula where it enters the chest cavity and flows through the abdomen to GB 24. It travels up to GB 25, a point on the outside of the last rib. The meridian then runs farther up to the pelvic area, below the point of the hip to the hip joint. From here it passes over the femur and down the outside of the hind leg. GB 44, the Ting Point, is the last point on this meridian. There are 44 acupoints along the Gall Bladder Meridian.

GALL BLADDER MERIDIAN

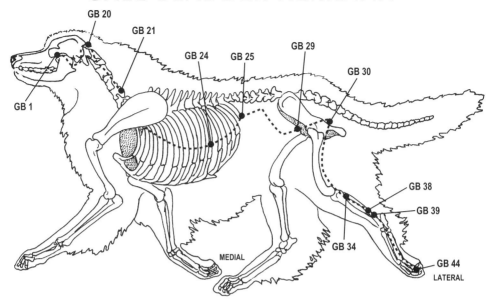

POINT	TYPE OF POINT *Traditional Name*	FUNCTION
GB 20	*Wind Pond*	Alleviates head and neck tension and pain. Helps with eye and ear problems. Nourishes the brain, improves memory.
GB 21	*Shoulder Well*	Relieves shoulder pain and arthritis. Use for hock pain. Softens tense muscles.
GB 24	Alarm Point for the gall bladder *Sun and Moon*	Use to relieve stomach indigestion and disorders, abdominal pain and muscle soreness.
GB 25	Alarm Point for the kidney *Capital Door*	For kidney disorders and lower back pain.
GB 29	*Squatting Crevice*	For disorders of joints, especially the hip joints.
GB 30	*Jumping Circle*	For hip soreness or dysplasia and sciatica problems. Relaxes the tendons and restores joint mobility.
GB 34	*Yang Hill Mound*	Influential Point for the muscles and tendons. Relieves joint stiffness.
GB 38	Sedation Point *Yang Aid*	Use for hock problems.
GB 39	*Hanging Bell*	Influential Point for building bone marrow. Use to strengthen the immune system.
GB 44	Ting Point *Orifice Yin*	Helps relieve arthritis and hock problems. Influences the eyes, relieves pain and swelling.

LIVER MERIDIAN
controller of strategic planning

SISTER MERIDIAN - Gall Bladder
MAXIMAL TIME - 1 - 3 am
ENERGY - Yin
ELEMENT - Wood

SEASON - Spring
GOVERNED PART OF BODY -
   Tendons, Ligaments
   and Muscles
COLOR - Green

INDICATORS

PHYSICAL

Eye/vision problems
Estrous cycle problems
Digestive problems
Joint Problems
Tendon and ligament problems

BEHAVIOR

Aggressiveness or anger

FUNCTION

The Liver Meridian maintains even and harmonious movement of Chi throughout the body. It is the principal center of metabolism. The Liver Meridian controls hundreds of functions including synthesizing proteins, neutralizing poisons, assisting in the regulation of blood sugar levels and secreting bile. It also governs the flow of Chi in three ways: coordinating digestion and estrous cycles, and harmonizing the emotions. In traditional terms, the Liver Meridian is known as the *Controller of Strategic Planning*.

A balanced Liver Meridian allows both dog and human to use energy efficiently. The parts of the body associated with the Liver Meridian are the tendons and ligaments. A dog with smooth and unobstructed flow of Chi through his Liver Meridian will exhibit a flexibility of movement and an even temperament.

LOCATION

The Liver Meridian begins at a point on the first toe. This point is the Ting Point, Liv 1. The meridian travels up the inside middle of the hind leg, over the hock and up the femur. The meridian enters the groin region and travels toward the front of the dog. Liv 13 is located at the end of the next to the last rib. The meridian then slants down and ends with Liv 14. There are 14 acupoints along the Liver Meridian.

LIVER MERIDIAN

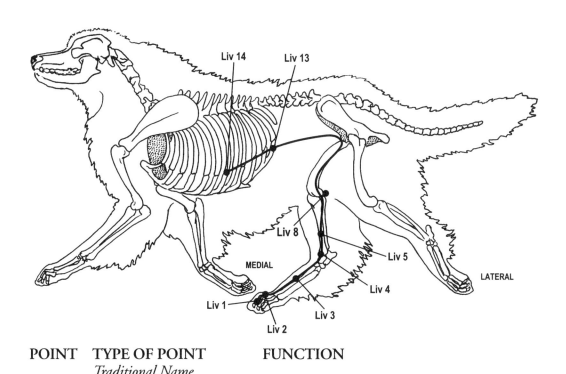

POINT	TYPE OF POINT *Traditional Name*	FUNCTION
Liv 1	Ting Point *Big Thick*	Emergency point, use to restore consciousness.
Liv 2	Sedation Point *Temporary In-Between*	Relieves diarrhea. Spreads Liver Chi, clears heat and stops bleeding. Relieves lumbar pain.
Liv 3	Source Point *Bigger Rushing*	Invigorates and clears the meridian system. Helps eye problems. Calming point.
Liv 4	*Middle Seal*	Relieves pain in lower abdomen. Use for stomach upset and reproductive disorders.
Liv 5	Connecting Point *Gourd Ditch*	Helps resolve irregular estrous cycles. Relieves emotional tension.
Liv 8	Tonification Point *Spring and Bend*	Relieves medial stifle problems.
Liv 14	Alarm Point for the liver *Cyclic Gate*	Helps with liver problems. Use for muscle soreness.

CONCEPTION VESSEL MERIDIAN
vessel gathering the yin

SISTER MERIDIAN - None

ENERGY - Yin

AREAS OF INFLUENCE - Abdomen, Thorax, Lungs, Throat and Face

INDICATORS

PHYSICAL
Genital disorders
Problems of the lungs and chest
Reproductive system ailments
Head and neck pain
Itching
Abdominal pain

BEHAVIOR
Anxiety
Hyperactivity

FUNCTION

The Conception Vessel Meridian affects all the energy of the dog's body and is responsible for controlling the Yin energy of an animal. In TCM it is said that the Conception Vessel regulates the peripheral nervous system. The Conception Vessel absorbs overflow energy from one meridian and redirects it to deficient meridians, thus balancing the energy throughout the body. Also, the Conception Vessel impacts all reproductive functions.

LOCATION

The Conception Vessel Meridian travels the full length of the ventral midline on the dog's body. The meridian begins at a point below the anus (CV 1). It runs between the hind legs, through the genitals and umbilicus, continuing along the midline of the abdomen and through the chest. It then passes up the midline of the neck and head and ends at a point on the lower lip known as CV 24. NOTE: This meridian does not have a sister meridian. The Conception Vessel Meridian has 24 acupoints along its pathway.

CONCEPTION VESSEL MERIDIAN

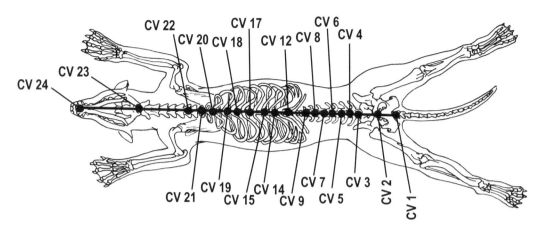

VENTRAL VIEW

POINT	TYPE OF POINT *Traditional Name*	FUNCTION
CV 3	Alarm Point for the Bladder *Middle Extremity*	Meeting of the three Yin meridians: Spleen, Kidney and Liver. Use to relieve incontinence, regulates the uterus.
CV 4	Alarm Point for Small Intestine *Gate to the Original Chi*	Helps urogenital problems.Strengthens the body and mind. Powerful calming point. Use to treat chronic diseases.
CV 5	Alarm Point for Triple Heater *Stonedoor*	Relieves abdominal edema, difficult urination or vaginal discharge.
CV 6	*Sea of Chi*	Benefits Chi as a general tonifiying effect. Use for a tired, lethargic or depressed dog. Relieves lower abdominal pain.
CV 12	*Middle of Epigastrium*	Influential Point for all Yang organs. Harmonizes the stomach, relieves gastrointestinal problems and relieves stress.Reduces heart irregularity and stomach stress. Helpful in dealing with behavioral problems.
CV 14	Alarm Point for the Heart *Great Palace*	Calms the mind. Regulates the heart and alleviates pain.
CV 15	*Dove Tail*	Powerful calming action for anxiety and emotional upsets.
CV 17	Alarm Point for Pericardium *Middle of Chest*	Influential Point for Chi. Use to improve overall energy of your dog.Use for all lung conditions, especially chronic problems. Stimulation of this point will increase or disperse energy, depending on your dog's current needs.
CV 22	*Heaven's Projection*	Strengthens the brain and regulates the lungs and throat. Effective for respiratory problems.

GOVERNING VESSEL MERIDIAN
vessel gathering the yang

SISTER MERIDIAN - None

ENERGY - Yang

AREAS OF INFLUENCE - Head, Back, Spine, Back of neck

INDICATORS

<u>PHYSICAL</u>

Spinal problems, backache

Hindquarter lameness

Nervous disorders

Immune stimulation

<u>BEHAVIOR</u>

Hyperactivity

FUNCTION

The Governing Vessel Meridian helps to strengthen the back and spine. It also controls the bladder and assists in coordinating and harmonizing all the organs and regions of the dog's body. The Governing Vessel is said to regulate the central nervous system including the brain, spinal cord and the spinal vertebrae. Like the Conception Vessel, the Governing Vessel acts to redistribute and balance the body's Chi, particularly the Yang aspect of the Chi energy.

LOCATION

The Governing Vessel begins at the depression between the anus and the root of the tail, known as GV 1. The meridian travels toward the head along the dorsal midline of the back. It runs over the top of the head and face and ends at GV 26, a point between the upper lip and gums. NOTE: This meridian does not have a sister meridian, it runs along a single pathway on the body. There are 26 acupoints along this meridian.

GOVERNING VESSEL MERIDIAN

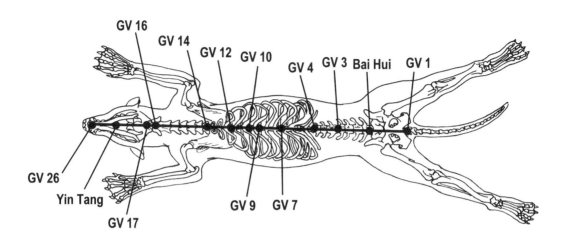

DORSAL VIEW

POINT	TYPE OF POINT	FUNCTION
	Traditional Name	
GV 1	*Long Strength*	Use for constipation and diarrhea. Can stimulate first defecation in newborn puppies.
GV 3	*Lumbar Yang Gate*	Strengthens the lower back and legs.
GV 4	*Gate of Life*	Intestinal problems and urogenital strengthening. Strengthens the lower back.
GV 12	*Body Pillar*	Strengthens the body. Use after a chronic illness.
GV 14	*Big Vertebra*	Meeting point of all Yang meridians. Immuno-stimulation point. Clears the mind.
GV 26	*Middle of Person*	Use for specific emergencies including shock, collapse, heatstroke, seizures or respiratory stimulation in newborns.
GV Yin Tang		Powerful calming point.
Bai Hui		Use for any hindquarter problem, heatstroke or over exertion.

chapter five

CANINE ACUPRESSURE POINTS

Dogs, we absolutely adore them, and there are moments we never want to see another dog for the rest of our lives. How do dogs have the audacity to look at us with such innocence after they have tracked inside all the mud from the base of the Grand Coulee Dam! What about the time Skippy had the brilliant idea of eating every single flower in the garden. Remember the day after Toga arrived, when she was eight weeks old and she rolled herself in fresh sheets then chewed her way out; that's how she got her name. Well, you have to love them, and chances are, if you're reading this book, you will never leave them.

Though dogs can bring us tears of frustration, we know in our hearts they also bring many blessings. Their gentle souls and simple joy remind us of who we are. Just touching a dog connects us with the better part of ourselves. When caring for their needs, we are also caring for our needs. As busy human beings, we tend to forget the basics of living; dogs never forget. When given the chance, even abused and neglected dogs remember how to love and be loved, to play and run for the shear pleasure of it.

Heaven goes by favor. If it went by merit, you would stay out and your dog would go in.
— Mark Twain

We have seen acupressure treatments make a big difference in both human and dog lives. Acupressure can help mend the most torn people and dogs. Learning the acupressure points, more commonly referred to as *acupoints*, is the next step to becoming a student of caring for your dog through acupressure.

Acupoints

Acupoint work is the core of an acupressure treatment. An acupoint is the specific place where Chi energy flows, often near the surface of the dog's body, and is accessible to manipulation. Acupoints can be viewed as pools of energy that when stimulated, improve the flow of Chi along a meridian. Although the specific acu-point is between the size of the point of a needle and a green pea, the area of effectiveness is thought to be the size of a dime or penny.

Usually, acupoints are located in the valleys of the body, not on a bony prominence or belly of a muscle. Acupoints are found in the depressions next to or between muscles and bones and around joints.

The purpose of performing point work is two fold: the first is to locate the potential imbalances in the meridian network; and, the second is to work with the points that will restore balance and harmony in the dog's body. An acupoint either can have excessive or deficient Chi energy. Using acupoint techniques, the practitioner releases or disperses energy that has become blocked, congested, or stagnant along the meridian. To bring Chi to a deficient area, you need to strengthen or tonify the acupoint. To reduce excessive Chi, you sedate the appropriate acupoint to disperse the energy.

> Acupoints usually are located in the valleys of the body, not on a bony prominence or belly of a muscle. They are found in the depressions next to or between muscles and bones and around joints.

Each of the twelve major meridians and the two Extraordinary Vessels have acu-points that TCM practitioners consider either as permanent or interim acupoints. Interim points appear during states of illness or injury and may or may not be located on a meridian pathway. Permanent acupoints exist at all times and are identified by their functions, locations and effects. The charts included in this chapter refer only to the permanent acupoints.

Acupoints are classified by their functions, benefits, and information they pro-vide when their specific characteristics are interpreted. Knowing and understanding how to use the different point categories during an acupressure treat-ment is a powerful tool.

Some acupoints have particular beneficial prop-erties. These acupoints are grouped together under a single classification, determined by the benefit these points provide. For instance, when the Master Point for the back and hips is included in a treatment for a dog with a broken hind leg, working this point can enhance signifi-cantly the impact of the treatment. Another instance: Because sister meridians

> A chart is a general guide for locating acupoints - not an absolute. Relax, feel the energy, and use your intuition to locate acupoints. Often acupoints feel harder, softer, more sensitive, or look different from the surrounding area or remainder of the meridian pathway.

are a reflection of each other, working with the Connecting Points on one meridian can "short-circuit" an imbalance of Chi on the sister meridian initiating a return to harmony.

Other categories of acupoints provide the practitioner with valuable information about the dog's condition. Each organ system has an associated point within the grouping of Association Points. If an Association Point is sensitive to the touch then you know there is an imbalance along the meridian represented. In addition, Ting Points can be used to ascertain the dog' s health and well-being.

The descriptions and charts identifying the acupoint classifications are on the remaining pages of this chapter. For detailed descriptions of acupressure point-work technique and further information about characteristics of acupoints refer to Chapter Three, Step-by-Step Acupressure Treatment.

Transpositional Versus Traditional Points

There is an ongoing debate regarding the exact location of acupoints. The two schools of thought are: Traditional and Transpositional. The Traditional school identifies points used on animals in China for over four thousand years. The use of these points is based on the acupoints' effects and are not necessarily associated with a meridian.

The Transpositional school recognizes points taken from the human meridian system and anatomically transposes the points to animals. The meridian pathways offer a guide or approximation to the location of

acupoints, although there are some anatomical differences that must be accommodated.

We, the authors consistently have used transpositional points in our practice, training and publications. We have found them to be an abundant resource for promoting healing. This debate is apt to carry on for many more years, but the real test is the results we have with our dogs. We encourage you to feel the energy in your dog's body and let your educated intuition guide you in the healing work.

ACCUMULATION POINTS

DEFINITION

The Accumulation Points are where the Chi energy actually accumulates. In China the Accumulation Points are called "hung" points; the word hung means great temples. The Accumulation Points are as spiritually and physically significant to the health and balance of the body as are the great temples to human life.

BENEFIT

Accumulation Points are where the Chi of the meridian gathers. These points are used primarily in acute conditions, especially if pain is present. Most often these points need to be sedated. Treating the Accumulation Points removes obstructions by dispersing energy and rebalancing the flow of Chi along the meridian. A beneficial property of all Accumulation Points is that they are said to help stop bleeding and relieve pain.

LOCATION

The Accumulation Points are located from the paw to the elbow on the foreleg and from the paw to the stifle on the hind leg. There is one exception, St 34, which is located just above the stifle.

ACCUMULATION POINTS

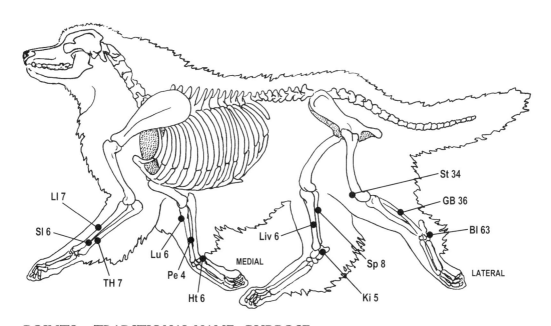

POINTS	*TRADITIONAL NAME*	PURPOSE
Lu 6	*Biggest Hole*	Acute respiratory conditions.
LI 7	*Warm Flow*	Relieves pain of rheumatism and tendinitis of the forelimb.
St 34	*Beam Mound*	Acute arthritis of the stifle, nausea or vomiting.
Sp 8	*Earth Pivot*	Regulates estrous cycle.
Ht 6	*Yin Accumulation*	Reduces sweating, relieves rheumatism of the forelimb and is a calming point.
SI 6	*Nourishing the Old*	Relieves acute elbow, shoulder or neck pain. Benefits the tendons.
Bl 63	*Golden Door*	Acute urinary problems. Relieves arthritis of the tarsal region.
Ki 5	*Water Spring*	Use to relieve hock pain.
Pe 4	*Cleft Door*	Calms the heart and regulates its rhythm. Excellent pain relief point.
TH 7	*Converging Channels*	Relieves neck, shoulder or elbow pain. Use for rheumatism of the foreleg.
GB 36	*Outer Mound*	Relieves stiffness, cramps or weakness of hind limbs. Relieves stifle pain.
Liv 6	*Middle Capital*	Relieves pain of rheumatism of the hind leg and relieves acute cystitis.

ALARM POINTS

DEFINITION

For each of the Yin/Yang organs there is an Alarm Point located on the ventral aspect of the dog's trunk. The Alarm Points received their name because they usually indicate an organ involvement or energy imbalance when they are tender to the touch. There is one Alarm Point that directly corresponds to each organ or meridian.

BENEFIT

A practitioner uses the Alarm Points in conjunction with the Association Points to differentiate between a meridian blockage or a possible organ involvement. Sensitivity to both the Association Point and Alarm Point indicates a possible organ or organ and meridian problem. Sensitivity to the Association Point alone indicates a problem along that meridian's pathway and no organ involvement. Check the Alarm Points and if one is found to be tender further examine the corresponding organ meridian. There are only three Alarm Points located on their own meridians, they are the Lung, Gall Bladder and Liver Alarm Points. These three organ meridian flows follow each other in the circulation of energy throughout a 24-hour period.

LOCATION

The Alarm Points are located on the ventral chest and abdomen, on the Yin side of the dog's body.

ALARM POINTS

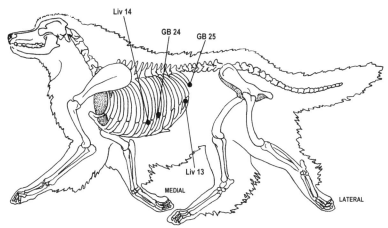

POINTS	*TRADITIONAL NAME*	ALARM POINT FOR
Lu 1	*Central Resistance*	Lung
St 25	*Heavenly Pillar*	Large Intestine
CV 12	*Middle of Epigastrium*	Stomach
Liv 13	*Chapter Gate*	Spleen
CV 14	*Great Palace*	Heart
CV 4	*Gate to Original Chi*	Small Intestine
CV 3	*Middle Extremity*	Bladder
GB 25	*Capital Door*	Kidney
CV 17	*Middle of Chest*	Pericardium
CV 5	*Stone Door*	Triple Heater
GB 24	*Sun and Moon*	Gall Bladder
Liv 14	*Cyclic Gate*	Liver

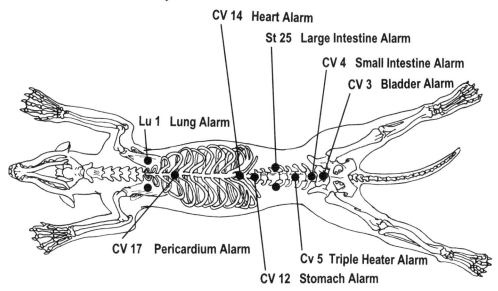

ASSOCIATION POINTS

DEFINITION

The Association, or "Back Shu" Points, correspond, or are "associated" with specific organ meridians. The points are named for their related organs. They offer valuable information, or "indicator" data, helping to identify where the imbalance resides and if the imbalance is acute or chronic. They are also used therapeutically.

BENEFIT

The importance of the Association Points in acupressure cannot be overemphasized. They provide a valuable indication system for gathering information about energy imbalances. Overall, the Association Points help balance and regulate the flow of Chi energy throughout your dog's body. These points affect the organs directly and are mostly used to tonify, or bring energy to, the organs. If an Association Point is sensitive to light pressure, it may indicate an acute condition. If the point is painful with deep pressure it usually indicates a chronic condition.

Association Points can help to balance your dog's emotional energy. If these points are chronically guarded, they can produce a physically stiff and emotionally resistant dog. Fear, depression and worry are emotional issues which may be released by working the Bladder Meridian. Because of these properties, it is beneficial for your dog to have the Association Points stimulated during most acupressure treatments. As outlined in the Alarm Points Benefit section, the Association Points, in connection with the Alarm Points help to determine whether there is a meridian imbalance or a possible organ involvement.

LOCATION

The twelve Association Points are located along the inner branch of the Bladder meridian between the shoulders and the tail of your dog. They lie on the Bladder meridian approximately ½ to 1½ finger widths on either side of the dorsal midline, lateral to the spinous processes.

ASSOCIATION POINTS

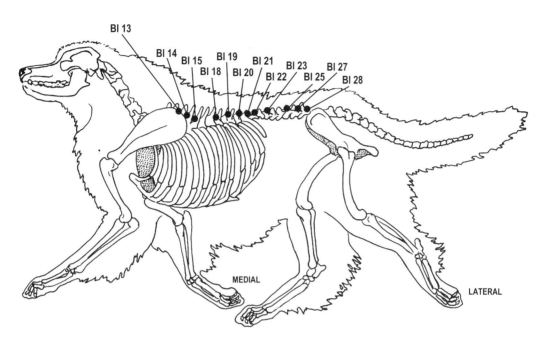

POINTS	*TRADITIONAL NAME*	PURPOSE
Bl 13	*Lung Back Transporting*	Lung
Bl 14	*Terminal Yin Back Transporting*	Pericardium
Bl 15	*Heart Back Transporting*	Heart
Bl 18	*Liver Back Transporting*	Liver
Bl 19	*Gall Bladder Back Transporting*	Gall Bladder
Bl 20	*Spleen Back Transporting*	Spleen
Bl 21	*Stomach Back Transporting*	Stomach
Bl 22	*Triple Heater Back Transporting*	Triple Heater
Bl 23	*Kidney Back Transporting*	Kidney
Bl 25	*Large Intestine Back Transporting*	Large Intestine
Bl 27	*Small Intestine Back Transporting*	Small Intestine
Bl 28	*Bladder Back Transporting*	Bladder

NOTE: Association Points are located approximately 1/2 to 1 1/2 finger widths off the spine.

COMMAND POINTS

DEFINITION

The Command Points correspond to the points of each of the five elements in the Five Phases of Transformation: Metal, Water, Wood, Fire and Earth. Each of the twelve meridians have five Command Points, one for each element. Therefore, there are 60 Command Points in total. These are evenly divided into 30 Yin points and 30 Yang points.

BENEFIT

Points are selected for stimulation based upon either the Control or Creation Cycle of the Five Phases of Transformation and the presenting problem of the dog. See Chapter Two, Traditional Chinese Medicine, for further information. Many practitioners use Command Points as their primary points in an acupressure treatment.

LOCATION

All 60 Command Points are located on the dog's front and hind legs between the foot and elbow and the foot and stifle. See the Command Point charts on the following pages.

METAL POINTS

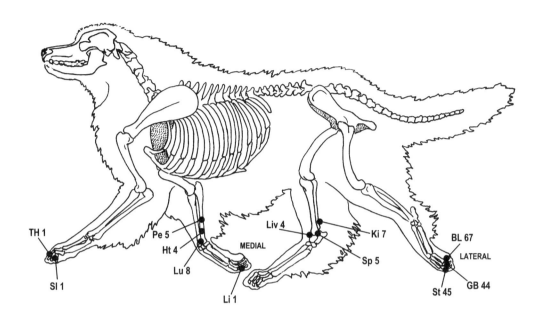

TH 1
Pe 5
Ht 4
Lu 8
SI 1
Li 1
MEDIAL
Liv 4
Ki 7
Sp 5
St 45
BL 67
LATERAL
GB 44

WATER POINTS

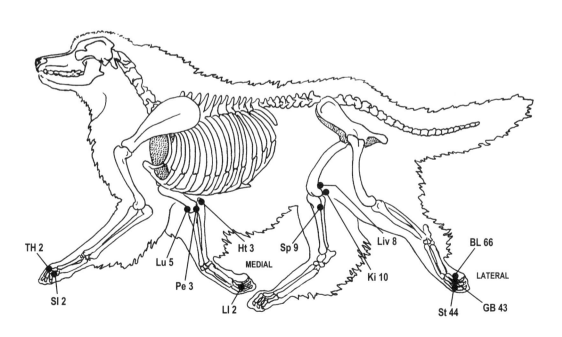

TH 2
Lu 5
Pe 3
SI 2
LI 2
Ht 3
MEDIAL
Sp 9
Liv 8
Ki 10
St 44
BL 66
LATERAL
GB 43

WOOD POINTS

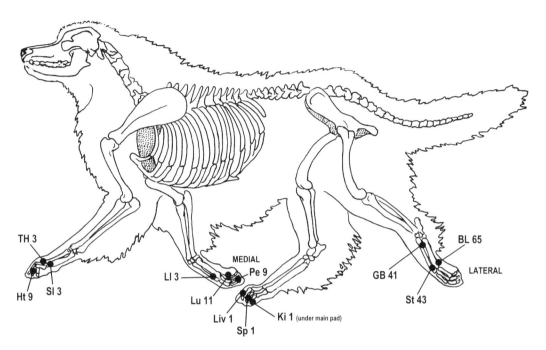

TH 3
Ht 9
SI 3
LI 3
Lu 11
MEDIAL
Pe 9
Liv 1
Sp 1
Ki 1 (under main pad)
GB 41
St 43
BL 65
LATERAL

FIRE POINTS

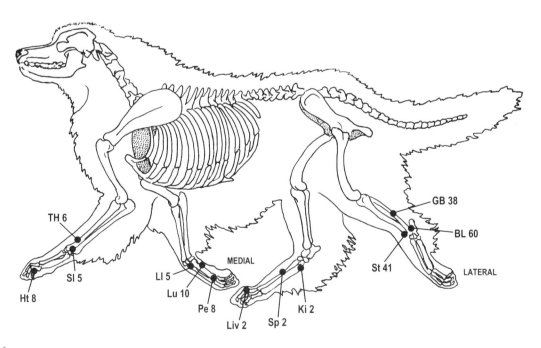

TH 6
Ht 8
SI 5
LI 5
Lu 10
Pe 8
MEDIAL
Liv 2
Sp 2
Ki 2
St 41
GB 38
BL 60
LATERAL

EARTH POINTS

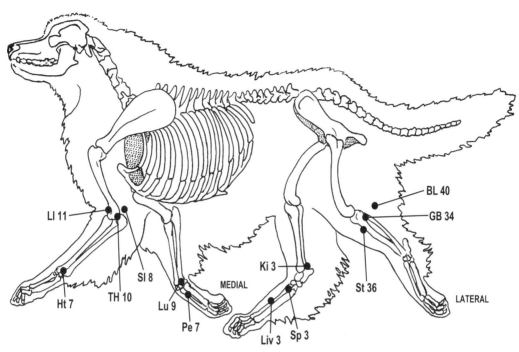

LI 11
Ht 7
TH 10
SI 8
Lu 9
Pe 7
MEDIAL
Liv 3
Sp 3
Ki 3
St 36
Liv 3
BL 40
GB 34
LATERAL

Frankie and Jacobi Jones

CONNECTING POINTS

DEFINITION

The Connecting Points, also known as "luo" points, connect the Yin and Yang energies of sister meridians. Stimulation of these points balances the Chi between paired meridians. Therefore, an imbalance of energy between the sister meridians may be resolved by using these points.

BENEFIT

Eastern literature on the subject says, the Connecting Point of the sister meridians behave as somewhat of a "short-circuit," allowing for the excess of energy to pass through the point from one sister meridian to the other. For instance, if there is a disharmony in the Lung meridian we can help balance it by stimulating the Large Intestine Connecting Point. The Connecting Points of a sister meridian are used in conjunction with the Source Point of the affected meridian. As an example: A dog with weak or deficient lungs may need the Lung Source Point, Lu 9, tonified. To enhance the Source Point's effect, the Connecting Point of the lung's associated meridian, the Large Intestine LI 6 may be sedated.

LOCATION

The Connecting Points are located on the fore and hind legs of the dog. See the chart on the opposite page for specific locations.

CONNECTING POINTS

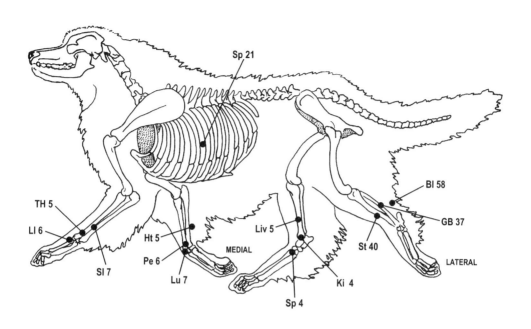

POINT	TRADITIONAL NAME	MERIDIAN OF CONNECTION
Lu 7	*Broken Sequence*	Large Intestine
LI 6	*Slanting Passage*	Lung
St 40	*Abundant Bulge*	Spleen
Sp 4	*Connecting Channels*	Stomach
Ht 5	*Inner Communication*	Small Intestine
SI 7	*Branch to Heart*	Heart
Bl 58	*Flying Up*	Kidney
Ki 4	*Big Bell*	Bladder
Pe 6	*Inner Gate*	Triple Heater
TH 5	*Outer Gate*	Pericardium
GB 37	*Brightness*	Liver
Liv 5	*Gourd Ditch*	Gall Bladder
Sp 21	*General Control*	Connecting Point for all Connecting Points

INFLUENTIAL POINTS

DEFINITION

Influential Points can have a powerful affect on a particular functional system such as bones or tendons. These points are indicated for use in an ailment or problem associated with each point's sphere of influence or benefit.

BENEFIT

The Influential Points are highly effective and are commonly used in conjunction with other points to positively impact the treatment. For instance, in an older animal with a long-standing arthritic condition that has led to bone deformity, you can use the following point combination:

Bl 11   Influential Point for the bones

GB 39   Influential Point for marrow

St 40   Influential Point for phlegm
         (spleen deficiency causing an accumulation of body fluids)

You may supplement these points with local points in the most affected areas. If the lower back and pelvis were involved, you can also add Bl 40, as the Master Point of that area.

LOCATION

See chart on opposite page for specific location of the Influential Points.

INFLUENTIAL POINTS

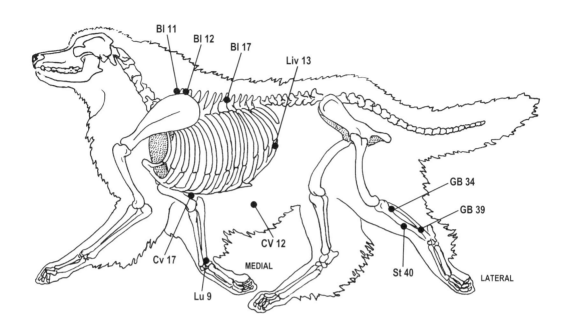

POINTS	TRADITIONAL NAME	AREAS OF INFLUENCE
Lu 9	*Greater Abyss*	Arteries
Bl 11	*Big Reed*	Bones
Bl 12	*Wind Door*	Wind and trachea
Bl 17	*Back Transporting Point*	Blood and diaphragm Builds the immune system
St 40	*Abundant Bulge*	Phlegm
GB 34	*Yang Hill Spring*	Tendons
GB 39	*Hanging Bell*	Marrow and brain
Liv 13	*Chapter Gate*	Yin organs
CV 12	*Middle Epigastrium*	Yang organs
CV 17	*Middle of Chest*	Respiratory system and Chi

NOTE: Conception Vessel points are located on the ventral midline.

MASTER POINTS

DEFINITION

The Master Points powerfully affect a specific anatomical region of your dog's body such as the head and neck, or the back and hips. These points may be used for problems or ailments within the region of influence of each point. For example, you may want to use Bl 40, the Master Point for the back and hips, if your dog has back or hip trauma.

BENEFIT

By including a Master Point that affects a specific area of the body where there is an illness or injury, you can significantly enhance an acupressure treatment.

LOCATION

The Master Points are located on the fore and hind legs, not necessarily in the area they impact. See chart on opposite page for specific location.

MASTER POINTS

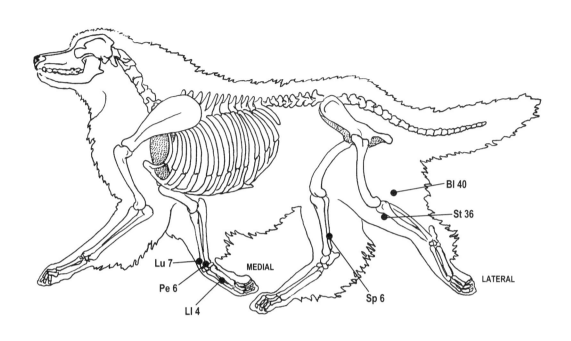

POINTS	TRADITIONAL NAME	REGION OF IMPACT
LI 4	*Joining Valley*	Face and mouth
Lu 7	*Broken Sequence*	Head and neck
St 36	*Foot Three Miles*	Abdomen and gastrointestinal tract
Sp 6	*Three Yin Meeting*	Urogenital systems and the rear portion of the abdomen
Bl 40	*Supporting Middle*	Lower back and hips
Pe 6	*Inner Gate*	Chest and front portion of the abdomen

SEDATION POINTS

DEFINITION

All twelve major meridians have their own Sedation Point. A Sedation Point can subdue or disperse excess energy within the meridian flow. Sedation Points are often warm to the touch and protrude slightly from the body of the dog.

BENEFIT

Sedation Points are used to disperse or decrease energy in a meridian. For example, in a dog who angers easily, you may want to disperse the energy in the liver. To sedate the energy, work Liv 2, the Sedation Point on the Liver Meridian.

LOCATION

The Sedation Points are located on the fore or hind legs of the dog along the organ meridian whose activity it governs. See the chart on the opposite page for specific location.

SEDATION POINTS

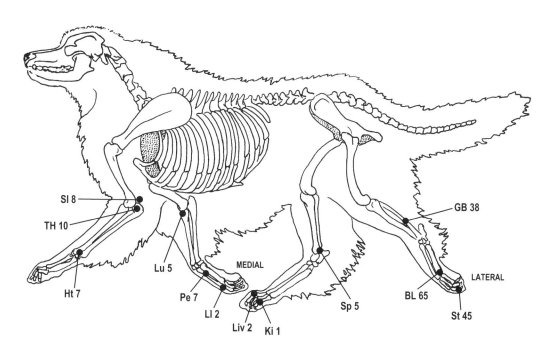

POINTS	*TRADITIONAL NAME*	MERIDIAN
Lu 5	*Foot Marsh*	Lung
LI 2	*Second Interval*	Large Intestine
St 45	*Sick Mouth*	Stomach
Sp 5	*Gold Mound*	Spleen
Ht 7	*Mind Door*	Heart
SI 8	*Small Intestine Sea*	Small Intestine
Bl 65	*Binding Bone*	Bladder
Ki 1	*Bubbling Spring*	Kidney
Pe 7	*Great Hill*	Pericardium
TH 10	*Heavenly Well*	Triple Heater
GB 38	*Yang Aid*	Gall Bladder
Liv 2	*Temporary In-Between*	Liver

SOURCE POINTS

DEFINITION

All twelve major meridians have a Source Point. They are identified by the organ on which they are located. The Source Point is located on an organ's meridian and can sedate or tonify depending on the specific need of the meridian at the time of the acupressure treatment. Swelling or deep dip at a point location indicates the need for Source Point work.

BENEFIT

Source Points can be used to determine if there is an excess or deficiency in an organ as well as restore the balance of Chi energy in their associated meridian. Source Point work can produce an immediate effect. In combination with a Tonification or Sedation Point, the effect of either point work can be enhanced.

Source Points are particularly effective in tonifying the yin organs. If your dog tends to have respiratory problems, in addition to the traditional treatment by your veterinarian, stimulation of the Lung Source Point can help to strengthen the Lung Meridian.

LOCATION

The Source Points are located primarily around the wrist and hock of your dog. See the chart on the opposite page for their specific location.

SOURCE POINTS

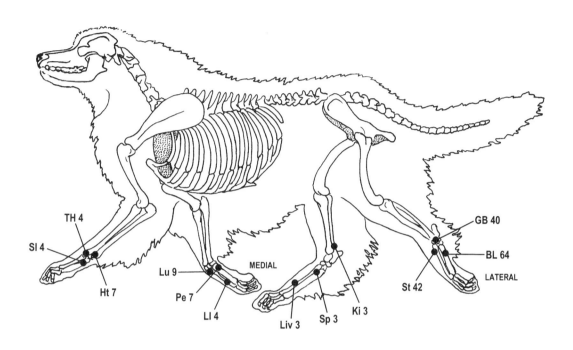

POINTS	TRADITIONAL NAME	MERIDIAN
Lu 9	*Greater Abyss*	Lung
LI 4	*Joining Valley*	Large Intestine
St 42	*Rushing Yang*	Stomach
Sp 3	*Greater White*	Spleen
Ht 7	*Mind Door*	Heart
SI 4	*Wrist Bone*	Small Intestine
Bl 64	*Capital Bone*	Bladder
Ki 3	*Greater Stream*	Kidney
Pe 7	*Great Hill*	Pericardium
TH 4	*Yang Pond*	Triple Heater
GB 40	*Mound Ruins*	Gall Bladder
Liv 3	*Bigger Rushing*	Liver

TING POINTS

DEFINITION

Each of the twelve major meridians has its own Ting Point. They are either the beginning or ending point of a meridian. It is important to view the Ting Points in relation to each other. Ting Points that are not balanced may look and feel different from the other Ting Points and surrounding skin. This may indicate that there is an imbalance in the Ting Point's corresponding meridian. If a point feels warm, slightly swollen or protrudes, it may be an excess condition and possibly an acute situation. If a Ting Point feels soft and dips or a pit is left after pressure is released, and other characteristics like dry hair or skin are present, there is most likely a deficiency condition and probably a chronic situation.

BENEFIT

Ting Points provide important information regarding the general health and well-being of your dog. It is possible to detect meridian imbalances and diseases by being aware of particular visual and tactile cues that Ting Points exhibit. They are very powerful points for treatment; there are practitioners who balance the whole dog by using Ting Points alone.

LOCATION

Ting Points are located on the front and hind legs of the dog. Each Ting Point is either the beginning or end point of the meridian it impacts most directly. See the chart on the opposite page for the specific location of each Ting Point.

TING POINTS

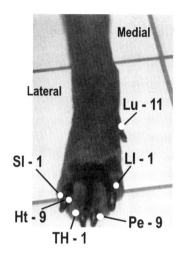

FORELEG

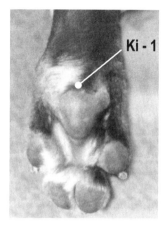

HIND LEG

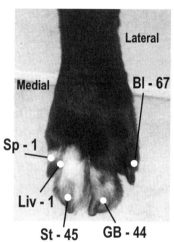

HIND LEG

POINTS	TRADITIONAL NAME	MERIDIAN
Lu 11	*Lesser Metal*	Lung
LI 1	*Metal Yang*	Large Intestine
St 45	*Sick Mouth*	Stomach
Sp 1	*Hidden White*	Spleen
Ht 9	*Lesser Yin Rushing*	Heart
SI 1	*Lesser Marsh*	Small Intestine
Bl 67	*Reaching Yin*	Bladder
Ki 1	*Bubbling Spring*	Kidney
Pe 9 (tip of 3rd toe)	*Center Rush*	Pericardium
TH 1	*Gate Rush*	Triple Heater
GB 44	*Orifice Yin*	Gall Bladder
Liv 1	*Big Thick*	Liver

TONIFICATION POINTS

DEFINITION

Each of the twelve major meridians has its own Tonification Point. These points are located on the meridian for which they are named. Stimulation of a Tonification Point will increase Chi energy in that meridian. These points usually feel cool to the touch.

BENEFIT

By working the Tonification Point you can increase Chi energy to the entire meridian and its corresponding organ. If your dog's Heart Meridian feels as if it is depleted, stimulation of the Tonification Point on the Heart Meridian, Ht 9, can add Chi energy to the Heart Meridian pathway.

LOCATION

The Tonification Points are located on the fore and hind legs of your dog. See the chart on the opposite page for specific location.

TONIFICATION POINTS

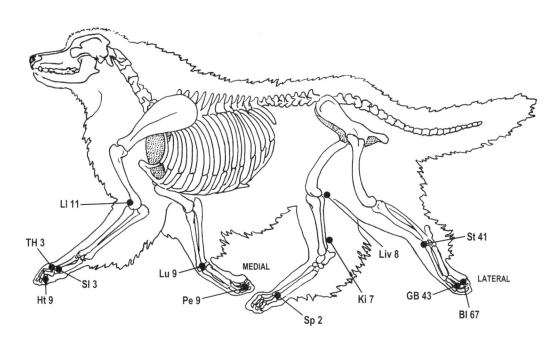

POINTS	*TRADITIONAL NAME*	MERIDIAN
Lu 9	*Greater Abyss*	Lung
LI 11	*Crooked Pond*	Large Intestine
St 41	*Dispersing Stream*	Stomach
Sp 2	*Big Capital*	Spleen
Ht 9	*Lesser Yin Rushing*	Heart
SI 3	*Back Stream*	Small Intestine
Bl 67	*Reaching Yin*	Bladder
Ki 7	*Returning Current*	Kidney
Pe 9	*Center Rush*	Pericardium
TH 3	*Middle Islet*	Triple Heater
GB 43	*Stream Insertion*	Gall Bladder
Liv 8	*Spring and Bend*	Liver

chapter six

CANINE STRETCH

We can learn a lot from our dogs about stretching. When they waken from sleep, or a nap, the first thing they do is stretch. Dogs take obvious pleasure in reaching, pressing and stretching their front limbs, contracting their necks, then arching their backs, followed by walking forward to stretch their hindquarters. Every muscle contracts and stretches in slow, languid movements. It looks so satisfying to stretch the way a dog does.

If dogs are so good at stretching, you may wonder why we have included a chapter on stretches? Human-assisted stretching is the fourth and final phase of an acupressure treatment session. The stretches described in this chapter:

- Relax and tone muscles to improve range of motion
- Increase flexibility to improve performance and avoid injury
- Reduce post-exercise or competition soreness
- Aid in the rehabilitative and healing process
- Enhance the flow of energy, relieving pressure on nerves.

The overall goal of stretch exercises is to maintain and improve your dog's level of fitness and flexibility, thus preventing injuries. Prior to a competitive event or training, athletic and working dogs benefit from stretches. People need to stretch before strenuous exercise; so do dogs. Additionally, we have seen many dogs' gait and confirmation improve as a result of consistent, manually-assisted stretching.

It is second nature for dogs to take good long stretches. As den dwellers, they stretched extensively in preparation for a day of hunting.

To get started with the stretch routines and complete your dog's acupressure treatment, decide where you and your dog will be comfortable and safe. With a large dog, probably it will be better to work on a carpeted floor or outside on the grass. With a smaller dog, working on a table or couch works well. The main thing is to find a place where both of you can relax and not be in awkward positions. Please be careful not to stress your own back while working on your dog. These exercises are supposed to be fun and a great way to stay connected.

If your dog is recuperating from an injury, illness, or is in advanced age, consult your animal physical therapist or veterinarian before implementing any stretches. Please follow their recommendations regarding the type, frequency, and duration of exercise that will be best for your dog.

GENERAL GUIDELINES FOR STRETCHES

▶ All stretching movements need to be slow and fluid.

▶ Perform all stretches on both right and left sides of your dog.

▶ Take the necessary precautions to be sure you and your dog are comfortable and safe during the stretching exercises.

▶ Stay within your dog's comfort range when assisting with stretches. It may take two to four weeks before you see significant progress. Be patient.

▶ Use consistent traction when holding your dog's leg in full extension or flexion; sudden pulling or pushing of a limb can cause injury.

▶ Proceed slowly through each of the stretches so they become comfortable for both of you.

▶ Close the stretch phase of the treatment to mark the end of the acupressure session. The energy of each meridian involved in your preceding acupressure treatment must be reconnected. To close and reconnect the energy, place your palm down on your dog, then gently stroke your hand over each meridian.

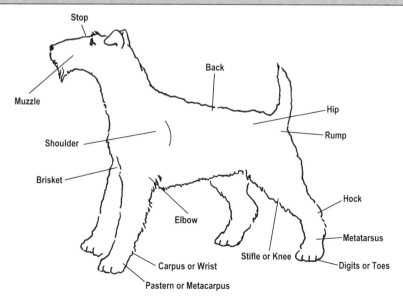

FRONT LEG STRETCHES

Front leg stretches are designed to relax and tone muscles as well as improve range of motion of the forelegs, particularly the shoulder and elbow joints of your dog. Dogs participating in agility events or herd working dogs often benefit from this series of stretches. These stretches can help open the energy flow of the meridians located along the front legs including the Lung, Large Intestine, Heart, Small Intestine, Pericardium and Triple Heater meridians.

The stretches shown for the front legs include:

- ‣ Deltoid and Triceps Muscle Stretch
- ‣ Shoulder Extension Stretch
- ‣ Shoulder Flexion Stretch
- ‣ Shoulder Rotation
- ‣ Shoulder Lift

When our canine friends are injured, they can benefit from human-assisted, gentle stretch exercise. Remember to check with your animal health practitioner before performing any stretching with your dog. A few good reasons to do prescribed stretches:

- Limited mobility such as bed-rest or wearing a cast can cause muscular atrophy.

- Scar tissue can cause a reduction in a muscle's movement and function.

- Muscle trauma can produce muscle splittting, a protective reaction, eventually resulting in the shortening of muscle fiber.

DELTOID AND BICEPS MUSCLES STRETCH

Repetition: 2 times

Initial Position: Sit facing the dog's back near his shoulders.

Exercise Steps:

1. Hold your dog's front leg at the wrist and gently stretch the leg toward the hind legs. Keep this stretching movement within the motion of a normal stride.

2. Bring the front leg back to the point where there is some resistance. Be careful not to pull the leg abruptly or beyond where you sense the tension of resistance.

3. Bring the leg forward slightly from the point of resistance and hold it there for the count of 8.

4. Replace the leg to its original position in a slow, even motion to complete this deltoid and biceps muscle stretch exercise.

1. Hold your dog's front leg at the wrist and gently stretch the leg toward the hind legs.

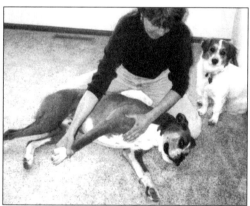

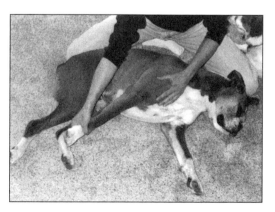

2. Bring the leg forward slightly from the point of resistance and hold it there for the count of 8.

SHOULDER EXTENSION STRETCH

Repetition: 2 times

Initial Position: Sit or kneel in front of your dog facing him.

Exercise Steps:

1. Place one hand behind the foreleg above the wrist and the other hand just below the dog's wrist.

2. Slowly lift the dog's leg until it is 6-8 inches off the ground. Vary the lift of the leg according to the dogs size. If it is a small dog, 3 inches may be the maximum lift you can achieve.

3. Gently bring the dog's foreleg toward your chest, positioning the dog for a full extension of his shoulder.

4. Carefully extend the dog's leg as far forward as he permits.

5. Release the extension slightly so that you are not stressing the leg, hold this position for the count of 8.

6. Replace the dog's leg to its original position and repeat.

Gently bring the dog's foreleg toward your chest, positioning the dog for a full extension of his shoulder.

SHOULDER ROTATION STRETCH

Repetition: 2 - 3 times each direction

Initial Position: Sit or kneel in front of your dog facing him.

Exercise Steps:

1. Hold your dog's foreleg, placing one hand below the wrist and the other below the elbow.

2. Slowly lift your dog's leg to the point of resistance and then lower it about one inch.

3. Slowly rotate the leg in a complete circle starting with a small, 2 - 3 inch circle, repeat 3 - 5 times.

4. Gradually increase the diameter of the circle to 4 - 5 inches, and rotate 3 - 5 times, then increase the diameter of the next 3 - 5 circles to 6 - 7 inches.

6. Reverse the direction of the rotation, counter-rotating the leg in 2 - 3 inch circles 3 - 5 times and gradually increasing the diameter of the circles for 3 - 5 additional counter rotations.

7. Replace your dog's leg to its original position and repeat.

1. Hold your dog's foreleg, placing one hand below the wrist and the other below the elbow.

2. Slowly rotate the leg in a complete circle starting with a small, 2 - 3 inch circle, repeat 3 - 5 times.

Please consider the size of your dog....

SHOULDER LIFT

Repetition: 2 times

Initial Position: Kneel at your dog's shoulder, facing toward his body.

Exercise Steps:

1. With one hand hold your dog's leg above the wrist. Place your other hand below his elbow.

2. Using a slow and even motion, lift the leg directly up to a point where resistance is felt. Ease off the resistance point, hold for a count of 5.

3. Release the leg slowly and replace to its original position.

4. Notice and feel the movement of the scapula.

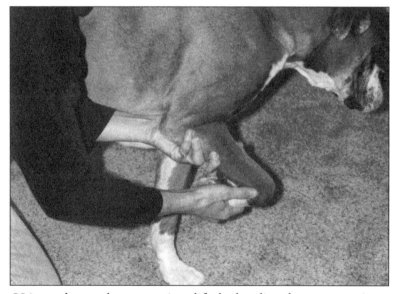

Using a slow and even motion, lift the leg directly up to a point where resistance is felt. Ease off the resistance point, hold for a count of 5.

HIND LEG STRETCHES

Hind leg stretches are intended to relax and tone muscles, improve suppleness and range of motion of the rear legs. Dogs who are involved with field trial, agility training or flyball can benefit from this series of stretches. They also aid in reinforcing the acupressure treatment by opening the energy flows of the hind legs including the Bladder, Kidney, Gall Bladder, Liver, Stomach and Spleen Meridians. After completing these stretches, remember to reconnect the meridians by stroking your hand gently down each of the meridians.

Stretches shown for the hind legs include:

- Buttocks Stretch
- Stifle / Pelvis Extension Stretch
- Hip Flexion Stretch

Courtesy of Crystal Glen Kennel, Fort Collins, CO

BUTTOCKS STRETCH

Repetition: 2 times

Initial Position: Sit/kneel facing the dog's back, hindquarters.

Exercise Steps:

1. Place one hand on your dog's upper thigh to support his knee.

2. Place your other hand below his hock and using gentle traction extend the leg forward in line with a normal stride motion. Stop when you feel resistance.

3. Ease off from the top of the resistance point and hold for a count of 8.

4. Place the leg back to its original position before repeating this exercise.

1. Place one hand on your dog's upper thigh to support his knee.

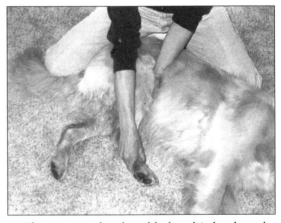

2. Place your other hand below his hock and using gentle traction extend the leg forward in line with a normal stride motion. Stop when you feel resistance.

STIFLE/PELVIS STRETCH

Repetition: 2 times

Initial Position: Sit/kneel facing your dog's back, hindquarters.

Exercise Steps:

1. Place one hand at your dog's flank.

2. Place your other hand on your dog's lower leg, below the hock.

3. Lift his leg so that his foot is 2 - 4 inches off the floor. Direct his leg backward in a movement that mimics a normal hind leg stride, then lower the leg to the floor.

4. Hold for a count of 8, then return the leg to a resting position.

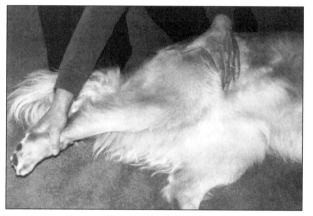

1. Place one hand at your dog's flank and your other hand below the hock.

2. Lift his leg so that his foot is 2 - 4 inches off the floor. Direct his leg backward in a movement that mimics a normal hind leg stride, then lower the leg to the floor.

HIP FLEXION STRETCH

Repetition: 2 times

Initial Position: Sit/kneel facing the middle of your dog's back.

Exercise steps:

1. Place one hand on his hind leg, below the hock.

2. Place your other hand on the hip area of your dog.

3. Gently bring his leg toward your body until resistance is felt. Hold for a count of 5.

4. Using the same slow, even motion, move the leg forward and touch the paw to the floor. Hold for a count of 5.

5. Now move the leg to the rear, touching the foot to the ground and holding for the count of 5.

6. Replace the leg to its original position before repeating the semicircular leg movements. Repeat stretch for opposite leg.

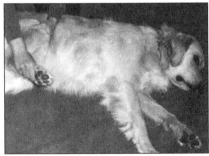

1. Place one hand on his hind leg, below the hock.

2. Gently bring his leg toward your body until resistance is felt. Hold for a count of 5.

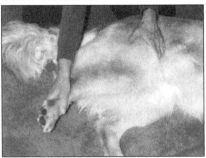

3. Now move the leg to the rear, touching the foot to the ground and holding for the count of 5.

BACK STRETCH

The back stretch helps build stronger abdominal muscles and increases the flexibility of the back. Stronger abdominal muscles will keep your dog's topline in shape and promote full use of his body. Your dog will respond to stimulation of the reflex areas by movement in his back. The best time to perform the back stretch is following an acupressure treatment when you dog is most relaxed.

NOTE: If your dog resists this exercise or shows any level of pain, do not continue. Consult your animal chiropractor, physical therapist or veterinarian chiropractor.

Repetition: 3 times

Initial Position: Sit/kneel at your dog's side, facing his abdomen.

Exercise Steps:

1. Place your fingertips on the midline of your dog's abdomen between his forelegs.

2. Wriggle your fingers while moving them down his midline from forelegs to navel.

3. To encourage your dog to flex his back, use only as much upward pressure as necessary.

4. Repeat 3 times.

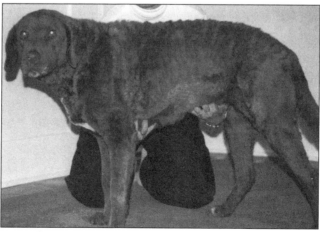

Wriggle your fingers while moving them down his midline from forelegs to navel.

113

chapter seven

ACUPRESSURE TREATMENTS FOR SPECIFIC CONDITIONS

Respecting and loving the gentle little souls that are hidden under fur and behind sparkling eyes is our job as humans. Unfortunately, a dog's life is comparatively short. Acupressure treatments add comfort and health to their lives.

Traditional Chinese Medicine (TCM) emphasizes the continuous transformation of all living things. Each of the Five Phases of Transformation represents a major segment in human and canine life-cycles. Life flows from birth, to growth, then to maturity, followed by harvesting the richness of our lives and storing or savoring life before passing. Dogs seem to have a natural understanding of the phases of transformation.

Puppies are born happy, and most are healthy. Their Chi energy circulates through the meridians helping them grow. Within weeks their eyes open and their ears start to take shape—they are entering the Growth or Creation phase of their lives. This first year of building toward maturity is important to create life-long health. If a puppy acts like the embodiment of joy, all the spiritual and physical forms of Chi are harmoniously providing their nourishing essence.

During puppyhood the focus is on a balanced lifestyle. Giving a puppy natural, nourishing food, exercise, training; and socialization with other puppies, dogs, and humans is usually all he needs. When energy imbalances occur in a puppy, it often relates to the stage of growth he is experiencing and is a normal imbalance. You do not want to interfere with the incidental disharmonies during this fast growth period.

There are a few acupressure treatments that may be needed during the latter part of puppy-

A few years ago, the New Yorker Magazine had a wonderful cartoon by Charles Barsotti. The image was a simple line drawing of a dog judge peering down over his bench at a remorseful little puppy that was cringing on the floor. The judge's determination was, "It's a puppy." Those of us who have had them know, puppies are puppies and that's the way it is.

Courtesy of Crystal Glen Kennel, Fort Collins, CO

hood. If you are not planning to breed your dog, most practitioners and trainers suggest that you neuter your dog at about six months of age. A treatment plan for Post Neutering is included in the Physical Conditions section of this chapter.

Puppies are usually pretty hardy, but they can contract infections, suffer physical trauma, or have an allergic reaction. The Immune System Strengthening treatment plan helps to balance the meridians that directly affect these ailments or conditions.

Maturity is the next stage of transformation. In the dog's life-cycle, he is considered mature when he is approximately eighteen months of age, has attained full growth potential, and is sexually mature. Most dogs are at the height of their physical and energetic prowess during early maturity. If you plan to breed your dog, it would be good to see treatment plans for reproduction. Hip dysplasia and other orthopedic conditions become apparent as the dog matures. These conditions eventually lead to arthritic problems. Specific treatment plans are included for hip dysplasia, shoulder soreness, and a few different underlying causes of arthritis.

Courtesy of Crystal Glen Kennel, Fort Collins, CO

TCM refers to the stage following maturity as "Harvest." A dog's middle years are when he starts to slow down. You know he is in the autumn of his life when his muscles are not as well-toned as they were and he is content to walk at your side. As the years progress into old age, your dog takes pleasure in his last days.

We have an elderly Golden living nearby. Sage is sixteen-years-old, which is very old for a large dog. She lies on her lawn quietly, peacefully smelling the new spring grass and watching her little world happen around her. When we walk by, she haltingly, but with no complaint, gets up to say hello, wags her tail slowly, then settles back down to her comfortable spot. Sage's white face shows her calm enjoyment of this period of her life.

Dogs, like humans, must contend with many physical and behavior/emotional issues as they pass through the Five Phases of Transformation. This chapter includes over thirty specific treatment plans that address many of the common indicators of disharmony of Chi that may occur during all phases of life. The chapter is divided into three sections: Physical Conditions, Behavior and Emotional Issues, and Sensory Enhancement.

Each treatment plan begins with the standard Opening procedure discussed in Chapter Three, Step-by-Step Canine Acupressure Treatment. Proceed to the Point Work portion of the treatment, follow with the Closing techniques and Stretches. Refer to Chapter Three as needed.

Conditions such as bloat, trauma, or shock, require immediate attention from your veterinarian. You can perform the acupressure treatment suggested in this chapter while your dog is in transit to the veterinary clinic. Acupressure is a complement to veterinary medicine, not a substitute.

Each dog is an individual with distinct energy imbalances. When you are working with your dog, you may find that he improves significantly after using only some of the points listed for the condition. Feel free to adapt the recommended Point Work to your dog's particular needs. After your dog has experienced a few treatments, he most likely will show you which points need attention, by scratching a spot, rubbing his body along a meridian, or touching his nose to a point.

There are two essential elements in acupressure work. The first is to trust your dog's and your own sense of healing. The second is to provide treatments consistently. When trust in your healing abilities is combined with ongoing treatment, the results are powerful.

An acupoint can serve many purposes, depending on the body's condition. Don't be surprised to find that a point is known for its calming effects, while it also relieves chronic tiredness, reduces pain and regulates the uterus and estrous cycle (Spleen 6, Three Yin Meeting).

Large Intestine 4, Joining Valley, has several healing attributes. It is listed in many treatment plans: Immune Strengthening, Shoulder Soreness, Pain Reduction, Arthritis, Constipation, Skin Conditions, Kennel Cough, and Vision Treatments. Rather than list all the attributes under each condition, only the applicable attributes are listed for specific conditions.

ARTHRITIS

TCM has demonstrated its capacity to relieve many arthritic conditions. Selection of a treatment plan depends on where the arthritis is located and under the condition it appears. After observing when and where your dog's arthritis is exhibited, select the appropriate treatment.

INDICATORS

Specific joint soreness or inflammation   Heat around the joints
Stiff or impeded movement of joints   Difficulty climbing stairs

WORSE WITH COLD

PRESENTATION OF ARTHRITIS

Worse with Cold   Arthritic area may feel cold, joints andmuscles may be involved.

Procedure   Open the Stomach, Large Intestine and Conception Vessel Meridians along their entire length on both sides of your dog. Perform specific Point Work on **St 36, LI 10** and **11 & CV 6.**

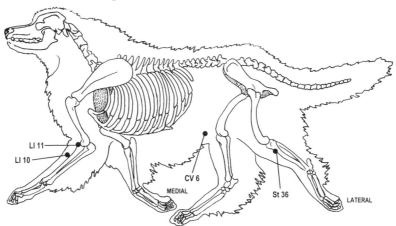

POINT	TRADITIONAL NAME	FUNCTION
St 36	Leg Three Miles	Tonification Point. Benefits the immune system and regulates the circulation of Chi.
LI 10	Hand Three Miles	Relieves arthritic conditions, particularly of the elbow.
LI 11	Pond on the Curve	Tonification Point. Benefits the immune system,use for arthritic conditions.
CV 6	Sea of Chi	Benefits Chi as a general tonifying effect.

JOINTS EXHIBIT HEAT

PRESENTATION OF ARTHRITIS

Joints exhibit Heat   Arthritis presents suddenly, joints are swollen and painful. Pain increases with pressure.

Procedure   Open the Large Intestine, Stomach and Governing Vessel Meridians along their entire length on both sides of your dog. Perform specific on **LI 4** and **11**, **St 44** and **GV 14**.

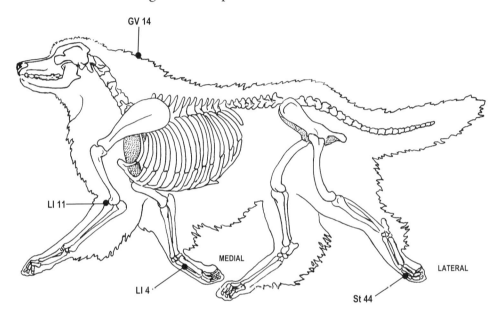

POINT	*TRADITIONAL NAME*	FUNCTION
LI 4	*Joining Valley*	Source Point. Relieves pain in any part of the body.
LI 11	*Pond on the Curve*	Tonification Point. Benefits the immune system, use for arthritic conditions.
St 44	*Inner Courtyard*	Use for arthritic conditions, clears heat.
GV 14	*Big Vertebra*	Meeting point of all Yang meridians. Strengthens the immune system and clears heat.

WORSE IN WET WEATHER

PRESENTATION OF ARTHRITIS

Worse in
Wet Weather

Condition presents more stiff than painful. Edema around joint and down the leg. Living in a damp environment can cause this condition.

Procedure

Open the Stomach, Spleen and Conception Vessel Meridians along their entire length on both sides of your dog.
Perform specific at **St 36 & 40**, **Sp 6 & 9**, and **CV 4**.

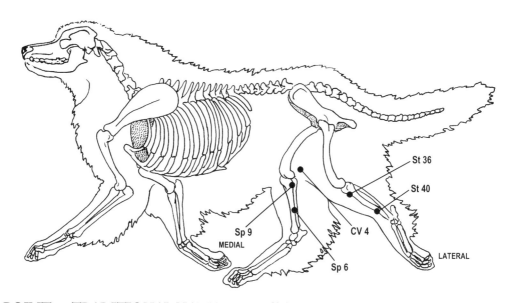

POINT	*TRADITIONAL NAME*	FUNCTION
St 36	*Leg Three Miles*	Tonification Point. Benefits the immune system and regulates the circulation of Chi.
St 40	*Abundant Bulge*	Connecting Point. Reduces hind limb swelling. Clears dampness.
Sp 6	*Three Yin Meeting*	Junction of three Yin channels: Spleen, Kidney and Liver. Benefits the immune system. Do not stimulate this point during pregnancy.
Sp 9	*Yin Mound Spring*	Benefits the Spleen and reduces dampness.
CV 4	*Gate to the Original*	Benefits the Kidneys and Yin. Strengthens the general energy level.

NOTE: Conception Vessel points are located on the ventral midline of your dog.

LOCATION OF PAIN CHANGES

PRESENTATION OF ARTHRITIS

Location of Pain Changes   Arthritic pain moves around the body. Muscles as well as joints are sore. May be worse during or after windy weather.

Procedure   Perform specific at **Bl 11 & 12, GB 39, TH 5, LI 11** and **GV 14.**

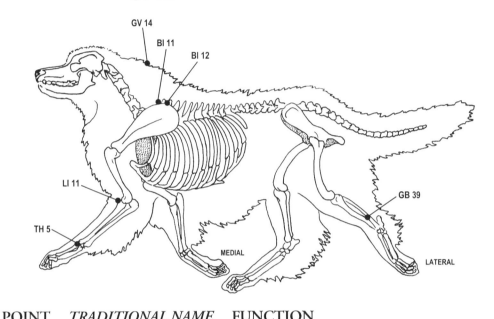

POINT	*TRADITIONAL NAME*	FUNCTION
LI 11	*Pond on the Curve*	Tonification Point. Benefits the immune system.
Bl 11	*Big Reed*	Influential Point for bone. Helps relieve arthritic pain.
Bl 12	*Wind Door*	Relieves cervical pain. Disperses Chi.
TH 5	*Outer Gate*	Reduces arthritic pain.
GB 39	*Hanging Bell*	Influential Point for bone marrow. Strengthens the immune system.
GV 14	*Big Vertebra*	Master Point for all Yang meridians. Strengthens the immune system.

GASTROINTESTINAL DISORDERS

Consult your veterinarian if your dog is experiencing diarrhea or constipation for even a short period of time. Diarrhea can cause dehydration very quickly. Constipation can be caused by a bowel obstruction.

CONSTIPATION

INDICATORS

Difficult, infrequent or absent bowel movement

Loss of appetite, vomiting, dehydration or a hunched back due to a tummy ache.

PROCEDURE

Open the Large Intestine, Bladder, Stomach and Triple Heater Meridians along their entire length on both sides of your dog.

Perform specific Point Work on **LI 2 & 4, Bl 25, St 36** and **TH 6**.

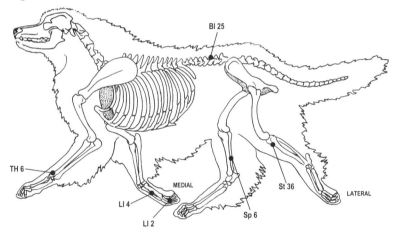

POINT	*TRADITIONAL NAME*	FUNCTION
LI 2	*Second Interval*	Relieves constipation by clearing heat.
LI 4	*Joining Valley*	Source. Benefits the large intestines, relieves constipation.
Bl 25	*Lg. Intestine Transporting Point*	Promotes excreting function of the large intestine, relieves abdominal fullness and distension
St 36	*Leg Three Miles*	Benefits the stomach and spleen.
Sp 6	*Three Yin Meeting*	Master Point for lower abdomen.
TH 6	*Branching Ditch*	Removes obstruction from the large intestine.

DIARRHEA

INDICATORS

Soft or loose stools
Abundant stools
Mucous in stools

PROCEDURE

Open the Large Intestine, Bladder, Stomach, and Spleen Meridians along their entire length on both sides of your dog.

Perform specific Point Work on **LI 4, Bl 20, St 25, & 36,** and **Sp 4, 6 & 9.**

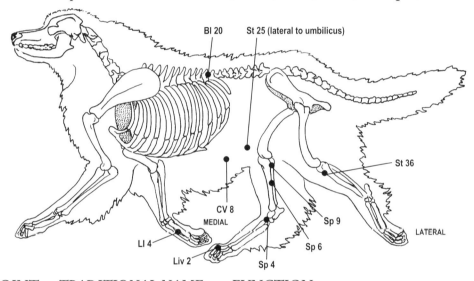

POINT	*TRADITIONAL NAME*	FUNCTION
LI 4	*Joining Valley*	Balances the gastrointestinal system.
Bl 20	*Spleen Back Transporting Point*	Calms digestive disorders.
St 25	*Heavenly Pillar*	Use for gastrointestinal disorders, relieves diarrhea.
St 36	*Leg Three Miles*	Benefits stomach and spleen. Strengthens the spleen.
Sp 4	*Minute Connecting Channel*	Connecting Point. Strengthens the stomach and spleen.
Sp 6	*Three Yin Meeting*	Master Point for lower abdomen. Strengthens the spleen and resolves damp heat.
Sp 9	*Yin Mound Spring*	Relieves diarrhea.

GASTRIC TORSION

If your dog shows signs of Bloat or Gastric Torsion, contact your veterinarian *immediately*. This condition is an acute life threatening situation. You can work the points noted in the Specific Condition for Shock on page 148 while in transit to your veterinary clinic.

The specific causes of this disease are unknown. Overeating, especially dry food, and an excessive intake of water are suggested to be predisposing factors. Torsion occurs more often in the large or giant breeds.

INDICATORS

Swollen, distended stomach
Drools and attempts to vomit
Exhibits pain, extreme discomfort

HIP DYSPLASIA

Hip Dysplasia is a painful malformation of the hip joint which becomes apparent as the dog matures. Although diet is considered a contributing factor, some dogs have an hereditary predisposition to developing hip dysplasia and other orthopedic conditions. The suggested Point Work for hip dysplasia addresses pain reduction, bone and joint issues, associated arthritis and strengthening of the immune system.

INDICATORS

Restricted hind limb mobility, lameness
Reluctance to jump
Difficulty getting up or lying down
Hindquarter stiffness and sensitivity to touch

PROCEDURE

Open the Bladder, Stomach, Spleen, Gall Bladder and Liver Meridians along their entire length on both sides of your dog.

Perform specific Point Work on **Bl 11, 40 & 60, St 40, Sp 9, St 40, GB 29, 30 & 34** and **Liv 3.**

NOTE: Along with the acupressure treatment, an Animal Chiropractor is often helpful with resolving this condition

HIP DYSPLASIA

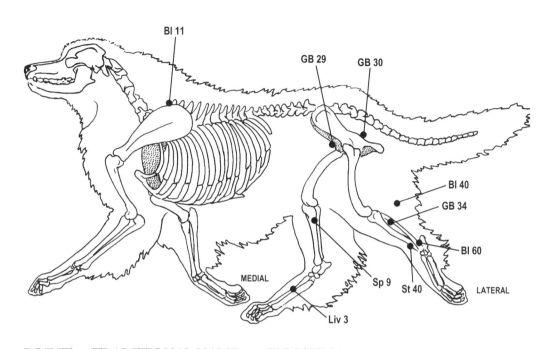

POINT	*TRADITIONAL NAME*	FUNCTION
Bl 11	*Big Reed*	Use for any bone or joint disorder, enhances bone healing and dispels wind.
Bl 40	*Entrusting Middle*	Master Point for lower back and hips. Use for arthritis in stifle, hip and lower back.
Bl 60	*Kunlun Mountain*	Aspirin Point. Use for arthritic conditions.
St 40	*Abundant Bulge*	Resolves dampness.
Sp 9	*Yin Mound Spring*	Use for pelvic problems, resolves dampness.
GB 29	*Squatting Crevice*	Use for disorders of joints, especially the hip joints.
GB 30	*Jumping Circle*	Use for hip soreness or dysplasia problems. Relaxes tendons and restores joint mobility.
GB 34	*Yang Spring Mound*	Relieves joint stiffness. Influential Point for the muscles and tendons.
Liv 3	*Bigger Rushing*	Relieves muscle spasms.

IMMUNE SYSTEM STRENGTHENING

INDICATORS

Frequent low-level infections
Exhibiting allergic conditions (eye or nasal discharge, chronic skin problems)
Exposure to animals with contagious conditions
Following a surgery, trauma or a vaccination reaction

PROCEDURE

Open the Large Intestine, Bladder, Stomach, Spleen, Kidney, Governing and Conception Vessel Meridians along their entire length on both sides of your dog.

Perform specific Point Work on **LI 4 & 11, Bl 18 & 23, St 36, Sp 6, Ki 27, CV 6** and **GV 14.**

Courtesy of Crystal Glen Kennel, Fort Collins, CO

FREQUENCY

Administer this acupressure treatment twice a week or until the condition improves, then only as needed. Consult your veterinarian for diet and/or supplements that will also strengthen your dog's immune system.

IMMUNE SYSTEM STRENGTHENING

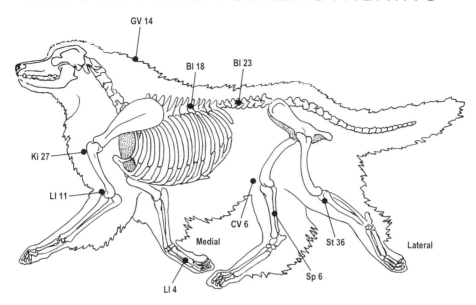

POINT	*TRADITIONAL NAME*	FUNCTION
LI 4	*Joining Valley*	Strengthens the immune system.
LI 11	*Pond on the Curve*	Relieves immune system weakness.
Bl 18	*Liver Back Transporting Point*	Supports liver as a detoxifying organ.
Bl 23	*Kidney Back Transporting Point*	Strengthens the immune system. Nourishes blood and Kidney essence. Supports blood and Kidney essence. Supports detoxification of kidneys.
St 36	*Leg Three Miles*	Restores and strengthens the immune system.
Sp 6	*Three Yin Meeting*	Stimulates the body's immune system. Relieves chronic tiredness.
Ki 27	*Elegant Mansion*	Strengthens the immune system and relieves chest congestion.
CV 6	*Sea of Energy*	Strengthens the immune system and internal organs.
GV 14	*Big Vertebra*	Strengthens the immune system.

LOWER BACK SORENESS

INDICATORS

Resistance to touch or brushing on the lower back
Difficulty climbing or descending stairs
Difficulty lying down or getting up
Uneven hind leg stride

PROCEDURE

Open the Bladder, Gall Bladder and Governing Vessel Meridians along their entire length on both sides of your dog.

Perform specific Point Work on **Bl 20, 23, 24, 25, 27, 40 & 67, GB 29, 34 & 44, GV 4** and **Bai Hui Point,** the lumbosacral space.

STRETCHES

Rear Leg and Back

FREQUENCY

Administer the acupressure treatment and Stretches every third day for nine days or until the condition is resolved. Perform the Stretches on one of the days between treatments, not on the same day a treatment is performed.

NOTE: Along with the acupressure treatment, an Animal Chiropractor is often helpful with resolving this condition.

LOWER BACK SORENESS

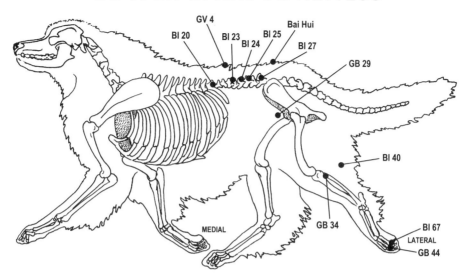

POINT	*TRADITIONAL NAME*	FUNCTION
Bl 20	*Spleen Back Transporting Point*	Relieves back pain and increases energy.
Bl 23	*Kidney Back Transporting Point*	Relieves chronic lower back pain and lumbosacral pain.
Bl 24	*Sea of Chi Back Transporting Point*	Relieves lumbosacral pain and moves stagnant Chi.
Bl 25	*Lg Intestine Back Transporting Point*	Relieves lower back pain.
Bl 27	*Sm Intestine Back Transporting Point*	Relieves sciatica and lower back pain.
Bl 40	*Entrusting Middle*	Master Point for the lower back. Relieves lumbar pain.
Bl 67	*Reaching Yin*	Ting Point. Benefits the lower back.
GB 29	*Squatting Crevice*	Relieves hindquarter muscle soreness and joint disorders.
GB 34	*Yang Spring Mound*	Strengthens the back and joints.
GB 44	*Orifice Yin*	Ting Point. Benefits the lower back.
GV 4	*Gates of Life*	Strengthens the lower back and helps chronic back pain.
Bai Hui Lumbosacral Space	*Hundred Meetings*	Relieves pain or lameness of the hindquarters. Use for pelvic or lumbar disorder.

NEUTERING OR SPAYING

As a responsible animal caretaker neutering your dog can add to the quality of your dog's life. Consult with your holistic veterinarian for the best time to neuter and what other natural treatments, food or exercise are available to assist in his healing.

The points noted below will benefit your dog post surgery. These are general pain relief, muscle, soft tissue injury and immune system strengthening points. You can work these points every other day. Pay close attention to your animals comfort level when working this set of acupoints. You do not need to do all of the points at every session.

PROCEDURE

Open the Large Intestine, Bladder, Stomach, and Spleen Meridians.
Perform specific Point Work on **LI 11, Bl 60, St 36, Sp 6, 10 & 21.**

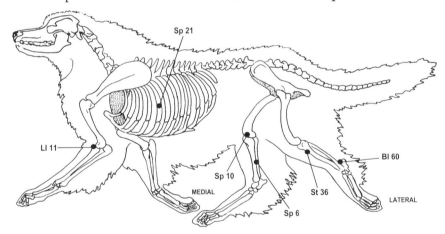

POINT	*TRADITIONAL NAME*	FUNCTION
LI 11	*Crooked Pond*	Tonification Point. Clears heat.
Bl 60	*Kunlun Mountains*	Reduces pain, clears heat and strengthens blood.
St 36	*Leg Three Miles*	Tonifies blood and Chi, strengthens body and mind.
Sp 6	*Three Yin Meeting*	Stops pain and moves blood, helps calm the mind.
Sp 10	*Sea of Blood*	Immune enhancing and blood tonifying point.
Sp 21	*General Control*	Reduces muscular pain throughout the body.

RESPIRATORY CONDITIONS

The points chosen for Bronchitis and Kennel Cough are to be used in conjunction with holistic or traditional veterinary care. If your dog presents either of these conditions, see your veterinarian immediately.

BRONCHITIS

INDICATORS

Rough cough   Lethargic attitude

PROCEDURE

Open the Lung, Bladder, Pericardium, Conception Vessel and Governing Vessel Meridians.

Perform specific Point Work on **Lu 5, 8 & 9, Bl 12 & 13, Pe 6, CV 17 & 22 and GV 4.**

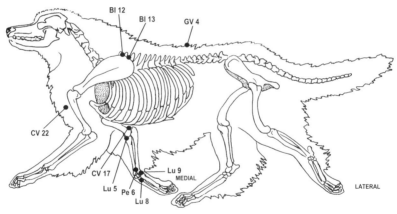

POINT	*TRADITIONAL NAME*	FUNCTION
Lu 5	*Foot Marsh*	Aids in respiratory conditions, dispels wind.
Lu 8	*Channel Canal*	Use to treat conditions of the throat and lungs.
Lu 9	*Greater Abyss*	Lung Source Point, transform phlegm.
Bl 12	*Wind Door*	Stimulates the functions of the lungs.
Bl 13	*Lung Back Transporting Point*	Strengthens Lung Chi, stimulates function of the lungs.
Pe 6	*Inner Gate*	Master Point for chest and cranial abdomen.
CV 17	*Middle of the Chest*	Clears the lungs, relieves fullness from the chest, tonifies Chi.
CV 22	*Heaven Projection*	Benefits both acute and chronic cough and asthma.
GV 4	*Gate of Life*	Nourishes Original Chi, relieves tiredness and lack of vitality.

KENNEL COUGH

INDICATORS

Intermittent dry, hacking cough
Nasal discharge
Reduced energy level

PROCEDURE

Open the Lung, Large Intestine, Bladder, Triple Heater and Gall Bladder
Meridians along their entire length on both sides of your dog.
Perform specific Point Work on **Lu 7, 8 & 9, LI 4 & 20, Bl 13, TH 5**
and **GB 20.**

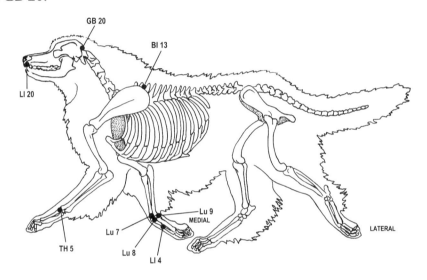

POINT	*TRADITIONAL NAME*	FUNCTION
Lu 7	*Broken Sequence*	Connecting Point. Use for acute or chronic coughs.
Lu 8	*Channel Canal*	Use to treat conditions of the throat and lungs.
Lu 9	*Greater Abyss*	Strengthens lungs, stops cough.
LI 4	*Joining Valley*	Source Point. Use to relieve congestion and coughs.
LI 20	*Welcome Fragrance*	Benefits colds, sneezing, stuffiness.
Bl 13	*Lung Back Transporting Point*	Strengthens Lung Chi, stimulates function of the lungs.
TH 5	*Intermediary*	Resolves phlegm and opens the chest.
GB 20	*Wind Pond*	Reduces colds.

SENSORY ENHANCEMENT

Dogs have keen sensory capabilities and humans often rely on dogs for their senses. Because of injury, illness or the aging process, these senses can diminish. The Sensory Enhancement treatments offered here can provide support in restoring your dog's sensory perception.

HEARING

INDICATORS

Not responding to loud stimuli   Failure to come when called   Ear pain

PROCEDURE

Open the Small Intestine, Triple Heater and Gall Bladder Meridians. Perform specific Point Work on **SI 19**, **TH 5 & 21** and **GB 2**.

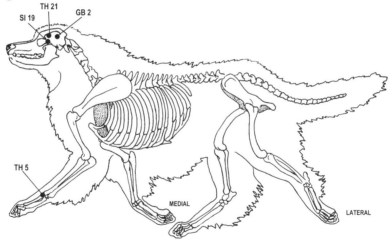

POINT	*TRADITIONAL NAME*	FUNCTION
SI 19	*Listening Palace*	Benefits the ears. Meeting place of Small Intestine, Gall Bladder and Triple Burner.
TH 5	*Outer Gate*	Benefits the ear, use for ear infections or hearing deficiency.
TH 21	*Ear Door*	Use as local point for ear problems and diminished hearing.
GB 2	*Hearing Convergence*	Important local point for ear problems and diminished hearing.

133

VISION

INDICATORS

Onset of cataracts
Lack of awareness of moving objects
Walking or running into objects

PROCEDURE

Open the Large Intestine, Bladder, Stomach and Gall Bladder Meridians.
Perform specific Point Work on **LI 4, Bl 1 & 67, St 1** and **GB 20 & 37.**

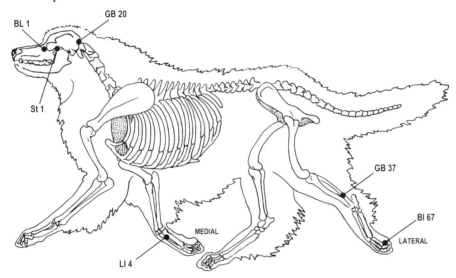

POINT	*TRADITIONAL NAME*	FUNCTION
LI 4	*Joining Valley*	Source Point. Benefits the eyes.
Bl 1	*Eye Brightness*	Benefits eye disorders of both internal and external origin.
Bl 67	*Reaching Yin*	Tonification Point. Clears the eyes of blurred vision or pain.
St 1	*Containing Tears*	Used for eye problems including, conjunctivitis, cataract and glaucoma.
GB 20	*Wind Pond*	Benefits the eyes Helps blurred vision and cataracts.
GB 37	*Brightness*	Connecting Point. Improves eyesight and removes "floaters" in the eyes.

ACUPRESSURE TREATMENTS LOG

Record the meridians, acupoints, and stretches you select along with your observations of your dog during each acupressure treatment.

Dog's name: **Date:**   **Time:**

Pre-treatment observations:

_____

_____

_____

_____

_____

Acupressure treatment observations:

_____

_____

_____

Opening:

_____

_____

Point Work:

_____

_____

Closing:

_____

_____

Stretches:

_____

_____

Post-treatment observations:

_____

_____

_____

_____

SHOULDER SORENESS

INDICATORS

Restricted forelimb mobility, not caused by foot or other leg problems
Shuffling gait
Lameness
Uneven forequarter musculature

PROCEDURE

Open the Large Intestine, Bladder, Small Intestine, Triple Heater and Gall Bladder Meridians along their entire length on both sides of your dog.

Perform specific Point Work on **LI 4, 11, 14 ,15 & 16, Bl 11, SI 9 & 11, TH 14 &15** and **GB 21.**

STRETCHES

Triceps Muscle; Shoulder Extension; Shoulder Rotation.

FREQUENCY

Administer treatment every third day for twelve days or until shoulder soreness is relieved. Perform Stretches on a day between acupressure treatments.

NOTE: Along with the acupressure treatment, an Animal Chiropractor or Physical Therapist is often helpful with resolving this condition.

SHOULDER SORENESS

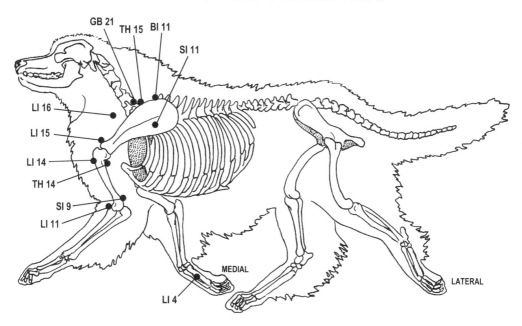

POINT	*TRADITIONAL NAME*	FUNCTION
LI 4	*Joining Valley*	Relieves shoulder pain.
LI 11	*Crooked Pond*	Benefits joint, relieves pain in shoulder.
LI 14	*Upper Arm*	Relieves shoulder tension and relaxes shoulder muscles.
LI 15	*Shoulder Bone*	Relieves shoulder and elbow arthritis.
LI 16	*Great Bone*	Benefits joint, relieves shoulder pain.
Bl 11	*Big Reed*	Use for any bone or joint disorder, enhances bone healing.
SI 9	*Upright Shoulder*	Local point to relieve shoulder pain.
SI 11	*Heavenly Attribution*	Local point to relieve shoulder pain.
TH 14	*Shoulder Crevice*	Helps relieve shoulder pain.
TH 15	*Heavenly Crevice*	Local point for shoulder problems.
GB 21	*Shoulder Well*	Relieves shoulder pain and arthritis.

SKIN CONDITIONS

In TCM terms, skin problems are seen as an excessive heat condition. The intent of a treatment plan is to reduce the inflammation and strengthen the immune system. The following treatment plans are general points and we suggest you consult your holistic veterinarian for these conditions. A natural diet, exercise and good grooming are contributing factors to the health of your dog's skin. In response to anxiety and boredom, dogs can obsessively lick or chew their own skin causing sores. Environmental irritants such as household cleaning chemicals, pesticides and fertilizers are also known to cause skin inflammation and toxic reactions.

ITCHY, DRY SKIN

INDICATORS

Excessive scratching, loss of hair
Excessive dander
Brittle and dry coat, lackluster condition

PROCEDURE

Open the Lung, Large Intestine, Spleen, Triple Heater, Gall Bladder and Governing Vessel Meridians.

Perform specific Point Work on **Lu 7, LI 4 & 11, Sp 6 & 9, TH 6** and **GB 20** and **GV 14.**

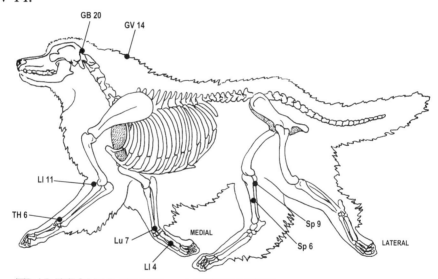

POINT	*TRADITIONAL NAME*	ACTION/USE
Lu 7	*Broken Sequence*	Connecting Point. Strengthens lungs, benefits skin conditions.
LI 4	*Joining Valley*	Source Point. Enhances immune system.
LI 11	*Crooked Pond*	Enhances immune system.
Sp 6	*Three Yin Meeting*	Benefits skin conditions.
Sp 9	*Yin Mound Spring*	Relieves allergic and toxic conditions.
TH 6	*Branching Ditch*	Benefits itchy skin and skin diseases.
GB 20	*Wind Pond*	Calms the mind, relieves the wind.
GV 14	*Big Vertebra*	Enhances immune system.

LICK GRANULOMA

INDICATORS

Excessive licking in one area
Eruption of red, open sore

PROCEDURE

Open the Large Intestine, Bladder, Spleen, Heart and Governing Vessel Meridians.

Perform specific Point Work on **LI 4, 5 & 11, Bl 11, 17, 23 & 40, Sp 9, Ht** 7 and **GV 14.**

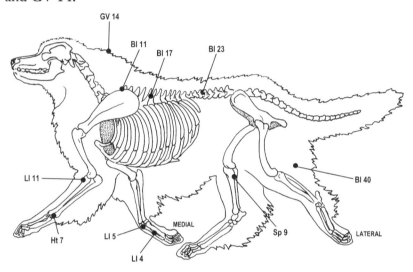

POINT	*TRADITIONAL NAME*	ACTION/USE
LI 4	*Joining Valley*	Source Point. Enhances immune system.
LI 5	*Yang Stream*	Stops pain.
LI 11	*Crooked Pond*	Enhances immune system.
Bl 11	*Big Reed*	Nourishes blood, strengthens Nutritive Chi, reduces pathogens.
Bl 17	*Diaphragm Back Transporting Point*	Benefits non-responsive skin conditions, relieves itchy skin.
Bl 23	*Kidney Back Transporting Point*	Stimulates the production of cortisone, anti-inflammatory.
Bl 40	*Supporting Middle*	Use to relieve skin condition characterized by heat.
Sp 9	*Yin Mound Spring*	Relieves allergic and toxic conditions.
Ht 7	*Mind Door*	Calms the mind.
GV 14	*Big Vertebra*	Enhances immune system.

TRAUMA

PAIN REDUCTION

The points listed below are *emergency* points and should be used while on your way to the clinic.

INDICATORS

Major physical injury

Trauma

Acute disease

PROCEDURE

Open the Large Intestine, Stomach, Spleen, Triple Heater and Gall Bladder Meridians along their entire length on both sides of your dog.

Perform specific Point Work on **LI 4, St 35, 39 & 44, Sp 6, TH 23** and **GB 36.**

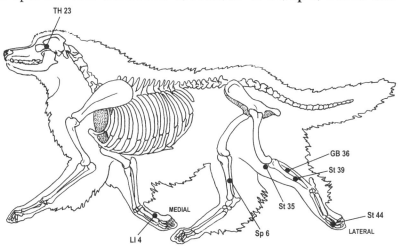

POINT	TRADITIONAL NAME	FUNCTION
LI 4	*Joining Valley*	Stops pain.
St 35	*Calf Nose*	Stops pain and relieves swelling.
St 39	*Lower Great Emptiness*	Helps stops pain.
St 44	*Inner Courtyard*	Stops pain and clears heat.
Sp 6	*Three Yin Meeting*	Stops pain and cools the blood.
TH 23	*Silk Bamboo Hole*	Helps stop pain.
GB 36	*Outer Mound*	Accumulation Point. Helps eliminate pain.

SHOCK

Shock, a condition characterized by collapse of the cardiovascular system, requires *immediate* veterinary care. The points listed below are *emergency* points and should be used in route to the emergency clinic.

INDICATORS

Major physical injury, loss of blood
Loss of consciousness
Dazed behavior

PROCEDURE

Open the Heart, Kidney, Triple Heater and Governing Vessel Meridians.

Perform specific Point Work on **Ht 9, Ki 1, TH 1, GV 26** and **Bai Hui Point**, the lumbosacral space.

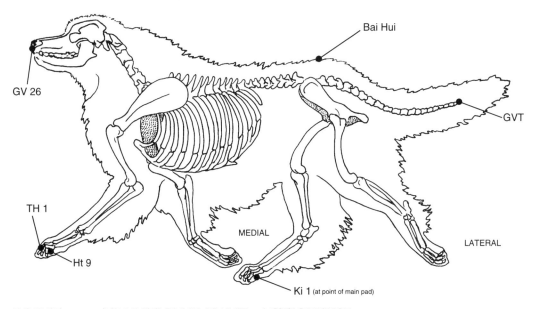

POINT	TRADITIONAL NAME	ACTION/USE
Ht 9	*Lesser Yin Rushing*	Restores consciousness.
Ki 1	*Bubbling Spring*	Clears the brain and restores consciousness.
TH 1	*Gate Rush*	Restores consciousness, stops convulsions.
GV 26	*Middle of Person*	Promotes resuscitation.
Bai Hui	*Hundred Meetings*	Promotes resuscitation.

BEHAVIOR

Dog behavior is a complicated subject. Left to their own world, their behavior is fine for a dog. When we bring them into our homes, they have to modify their natural behavior. We expect dogs to know, often with little training, how to act in our natural environment and be content with our lifestyle. As we discussed in Chapter One of this book, dogs have needs that do not necessarily fit into tidy, easy-to-manage packages. Living in our world can be very stressful for them. Dogs react to stress via behaviors that are not necessarily desirable or healthy. The following treatment plans address some of the more common difficulties.

AGGRESSION

INDICATORS

Excessive or inappropriate growling or biting
Extreme domination, initiating fights
Lunging
Fear/Apprehension

PROCEDURE

Open the Stomach, Heart, Kidney, Pericardium, Gall Bladder and Governing Vessel Meridians.

Perform specific Point Work on **St 40, Ht 7, Pe 5, Ki 9, GB 13** and **GV 11 & 24.**

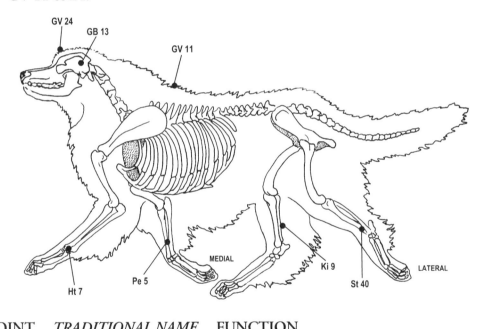

POINT	*TRADITIONAL NAME*	FUNCTION
St 40	*Abundant Bulge*	Calms and clears the mind.
Ht 7	*Mind Door*	Calms the mind, nourishes heart blood.
Pe 5	*Intermediary*	Regulates Heart Chi, relieves mental agitation.
Ki 9	*Guest Building*	Excellent calming effects, strengthens Kidney yin.
GB 13	*Mind Root*	Calms the mind, relieves worry and jealousy.
GV 24	*Mind Courtyard*	Use for severe anxiety and fear.
GV 11	*Mind Way*	Calms the mind. Relieves anxiety.

ANXIETY REACTIONS

INDICATORS

Compulsive, often destructive behaviors
Excessive panting and stress
Excessive chewing
Inappropriate ruination/defecation

PROCEDURE

Open the Bladder, Heart, Pericardium and Governing Vessel Meridians.

Perform specific Point Work on **Bl 10 & 15, Ht 7, Pe 6 & 7, GV 11** and **Yin Tang Point.**

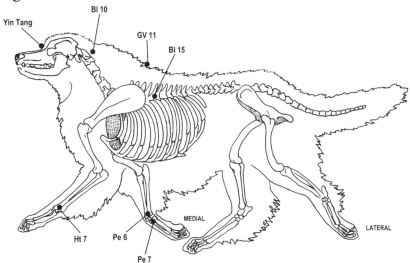

POINT	*TRADITIONAL NAME*	ACTION/USE
Bl 10	*Heavenly Pillar*	Relieves stress and improves concentration.
Bl 15	*Heart Back Transporting Point*	Calms the mind, relieves anxiety, stimulates the brain.
Ht 7	*Mind Door*	Calms the mind, nourishes heart blood.
Pe 6	*Inner Gate*	Connecting Point. Powerful calming action on the mind.
Pe 7	*Great Hill*	Source & Sedation Point. Relieves great anxiety and mental restlessness.
GV 11	*Mind Way*	Calms the mind, relieves anxiety.
Yin Tang		Relieves anxiety.

FEAR

INDICATORS

Inappropriate cowering, submissive posture
Biting

PROCEDURE

Open the Small Intestine, Pericardium, Gall Bladder, Liver, Conception and Governing Vessel Meridians.

Perform specific Point Work on **SI 7**, **Pe 3**, **GB 44**, **Liv 3**, **CV 15** and **GV 24**.

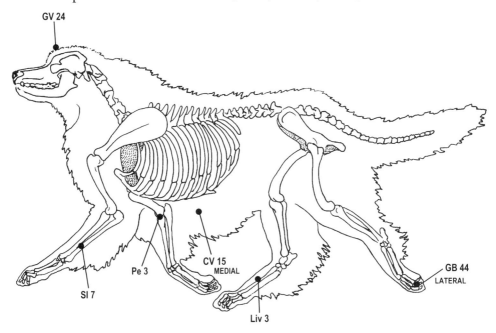

POINT	*TRADITIONAL NAME*	ACTION/USE
SI 7	*Branch to the Heart*	Connecting Point. Calms the mind in severe fear or anxiety.
Pe 3	*Middle Islet*	Tonification Point. Lifts the mind from fear or depression.
GB 44	*Orifice Yin*	Calms the mind, helps restore confidence.
Liv 3	*Bigger Rushing*	Calms the mind, helps relieve repressed anger.
CV 15	*Dove Tail*	Relieves fear, emotional upsets or obsessions.
GV 24	*Mind Courtyard*	Calms the mind, relieves severe fears and anxiety.

GRIEF/SADNESS

INDICATORS

Refusal to eat
Refusal to play, lethargic disposition

PROCEDURE

Open the Lung, Bladder, Stomach, Heart, Gall Bladder and Governing Vessel Meridians.

Perform specific Point Work on **Lu 7, Bl 23, St 41, Ht 8, GB 12** and **GV 14.**

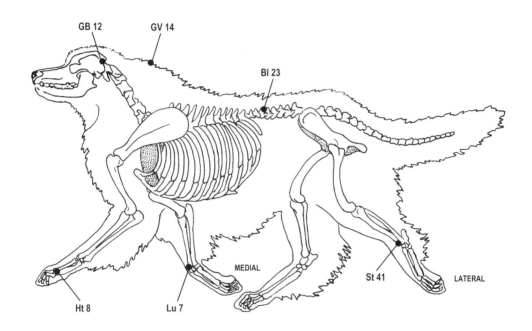

POINT	*TRADITIONAL NAME*	FUNCTION
Lu 7	*Broken Sequence*	Relieves sadness, grief and worry.
Bl 23	*Kidney Back Transporting Point*	Stimulates the spirit of initiative and lifts sadness.
St 41	*Dispersing Stream*	Clears and brightens the mind.
Ht 8	*Small Intestine Sea*	Sedation Point. Calms the mind.
GB 12	*Whole Bone*	Calms the mind, relieves sadness.
GV 14	*Great Palace*	Calms the mind and clears the spirit.

MENTAL CLARITY OR FOCUS

INDICATORS

Short attention span or inattention
Forgetfulness
Easily distracted

PROCEDURE

Open the Bladder, Small Intestine, Gall Bladder, and Conception Vessel Meridians.

Perform specific Point Work on **Bl 10 & 64, SI 3, GB 20** and **CV 17**.

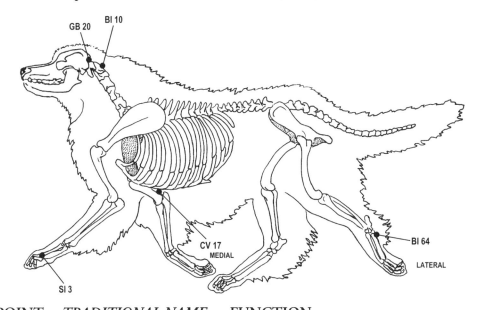

POINT	*TRADITIONAL NAME*	FUNCTION
Bl 10	*Heavenly Pillar*	Relieves stress and unclear thinking. Enhances concentration.
Bl 64	*Capital Bone*	Calms the mind, clears the brain, promotes
SI 3	*Back Stream*	Helps gian clarity of the mind
GB 20	*Wind Pond*	Gathers essence to the head, clears and calms the mind.
CV 17	*Middle of Chest*	Aids concentration, relieves nervousness and supports clear thinking.

The "O" Litter: Oak and O'Rourke

Two members of the Canine Companions for Independence's (CCI) "O" litter were welcomed to Denver by their puppy raisers in November 1996. Oak and

Oak

O'Rourke were two eight-to-nine-week-old, almost-white, soft and fuzzy Golden Retrievers. CCI sends puppies all over the country to spend a year with a family before being entered into its advanced training program where they learn specific skills to become a canine companion to people with physical disabilities.

Prior to Oak and O'Rourke's arrival, Janet and Jeff Bayless and I had been to CCI's Puppy Orientation classes to learn what we, as puppy raisers, were expected to accomplish in the year ahead. We learned specific guidelines, such as when we get up with the puppy in the middle of the night for the umpteenth time, we must take him out on lead. Then, we encourage his efforts by saying, "Hurry" and praise him to the stars when he toilets. For physically-challenged people, it is important that their canine companion toilets pretty much on command. The puppies have to wear their yellow-with-blue-trim capes in public at all times so that people will know not to pet them. We were instructed in CCI's canine commands and given a host of helpful training recommendations.

A puppy raiser's goal is to have the puppies return to CCI for advanced training when they are a little over a year old being well trained in "house manners." This means many things: they need to be calm around adults, children and pets, listen and respond to their handler, eat only when

O'Rourke

released to do so, and not be fearful or vocal. Starting out from ground-zero with a new puppy is always a mixture of fun, excitement, the constant questioning - "What have I gotten myself into this time?"

"The boys," as Oak and O'Rourke came to be known, looked so much alike and had so many similar behaviors, the Baylesses and I needed to support each other in our task of raising CCI puppies. Janet and Jeff were very conscientious about taking O'Rourke with them to grocery stores, restaurants, the movies, even to the court house to sleep on the judge's bench at Jeff's feet. Oak trooped all over with me. Everywhere I went, my caped puppy was my constant companion. Oak was easy going and took loud city activity in stride. He played and socialized with my other two dogs every day and went to weekly training classes.

Knowing that someone with physical challenges was going to experience the benefit of all our love and work made the months of training joyfully worthwhile. Unfortunately, the gods of dog genes had a different plan for Oak and O'Rourke. Both dogs had orthopedic problems. Oak had fairly severe hip dysplasia and O'Rourke had elbow dysplasia (OCD). When they were released from the CCI program, the Baylesses and I decided to keep our boys in the family. The dogs had their necessary surgeries and acupressure treatments to aid in their healing process.

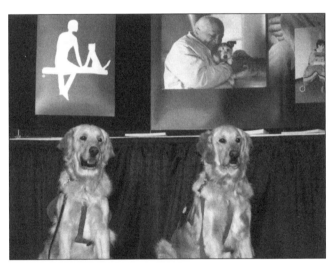

Oak and O'Rourke

Since the boys were so well mannered, enjoyed having a "job," and their temperaments were ideal for service, we decided to start them on a new career. Oak and O'Rourke passed all the tests for the Delta Societies Pet Partner Program and became Therapy Assistance Dogs. The Delta Society is one of the oldest groups in the United States to promote human healing through animal assistance. Oak and O'Rourke happily visit hospitals, schools for special needs children, and homes for the elderly. Wherever the boys go, eyes and hearts light up.

chapter eight

ACUPRESSURE MAINTENANCE TREATMENT

Ongoing acupressure treatments are as invaluable for a happy, healthy dog as they are for a sick or injured dog. Besides, this is your opportunity to have quality time with your best friend. Pick a consistent evening, or some other break time during the week to spend together. Take a leisurely walk, play fetch, then settle down to enjoy an hour of acupressure.

Offering your dog an acupressure maintenance treatment ensures that Chi energy flows freely through his entire body. Performing regularly scheduled treatments has been shown to increase mental focus and heighten physical performance for all types of training. The sensory experience combined with receiving personal attention from you—his most treasured human—is reason enough to work with your dog on a regular basis. If you need more justification to give yourself some down time to be with your dog, maintenance treatments help maintain your dog's:

- Balanced meridian system
- Vital immune system
- Well-lubricated joints
- Strong, supple muscles
- Overall sense of well-being
- Good level of energy.

Stress reduction is key for high-performance dogs like show dogs and competitive athletes. Acupressure allows the body and mind to relax, diminishing stress-related behaviors and pre-performance anxiety; plus, your consistent caring and contact with your dog helps build his self-confidence.

Through weekly repetition, you learn how your dog's energy feels and how your dog reacts to treatments when he is healthy. During maintenance treatments the emphasis is on opening your dog's meridians so the Chi energy flows smoothly. By gliding your hands over the meridians, you gain an awareness of how your dog's energy feels when his meridians are balanced. This knowledge of his body will alert you to any changes, giving you the advantage of addressing any sensitive areas or discomforts before they become serious blocks and cause greater imbalances.

It is very encouraging to perform maintenance treatments and see how much you are contributing to your dog's well-being. His health and performance usually will benefit by only one treatment a week.

Essentially, the maintenance treatment is similar to the treatment discussed in Chapter Three, Step-by-Step Canine Acupressure Treatment. Be sure to work in a physical setting that is familiar and comfortable for both you and your dog. If you are traveling to a show or competition, look for an environment that has some of the same spatial features as the feeling of home. Very important, clear your mind of the day's activities, or the past show performance, and focus on your dog. Formulate and communicate your healing intent to your dog.

PEANUTS

Treatment Log

Recording your treatments in a Treatment Log is a valuable addition to your treatment process. The Treatment Log can become a useful tool for assessing your dog's wellness, being aware of any seasonal changes in his health, and indicating how his training program is progressing. In addition, the Log can be helpful by providing information to your veterinarian, if the need arises. During each treatment, add comments regarding your dog's current condition, such as:

> ▸ Reaction or sensitivity to a specific point
> ▸ Areas that are particularly warm or cool
> ▸ Overall muscle tone
> ▸ Physical status
> ▸ Coat condition
> ▸ Mental focus
> ▸ General responsiveness and attitude.

Record your observations in the Treatment Log so you will have an ongoing record of your dog's reactions, changes, and progress. Specify the date, time of day, physical location, and description of the reaction, as well as the phase of the treatment in which the reaction occurred; for example:

> 9/9/99 - 2:00 P.M., Point Work - muscle spasms in the mid-neck area, lasting 6 - 10 seconds. Reaction was followed by lowering of the head, yawning, and licking his front paws. Closing phase, no muscle spasms, neck felt relaxed.

Maintenance Treatment Procedure

Please refer to Chapter Three, Step-by-Step Canine Acupressure Treatment, for a description of the Opening technique.

Opening

‣ Open the meridians on the front of your dog by stroking down his neck, over his shoulder and, using both hands, down the inside and outside of his front legs. Repeat this procedure on the opposite side of your dog.

‣ Open the meridians on the abdomen and back of your dog by stroking along his back and the side of his abdomen and flank; then, using both hands, down the inside and outside of his hind legs. Repeat this procedure on the opposite side of your dog.

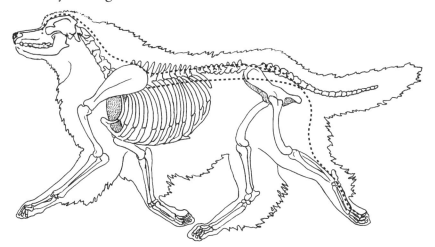

BLADDER MERIDIAN CHART

Point Work

‣ Work the Bladder Meridian on both sides of your dog because all the Association Points are located there. These points help balance your dog's Chi energy through out his body.

EXCESS ACUPOINTS	DEFICIENT ACUPOINTS
Protruding	Depressed
Warm	Cool or Cold
Painful or Sensitive	Vacant or Empty
Hard and Dense	Soft and Spongy
Acute	Chronic

▸ Note reactions and sensitivity to a particular point or area of your dog's body. Feel for areas of heat or coolness, protrusion or depression, sponginess or denseness, to determine if the points are excessive or deficient of Chi. If there are specific points that are excessive or deficient in Chi, additional Point Work is needed along the associated organ meridian. Generally, when a point is cool and depressed, it needs tonification. If it feels warm and protrudes, sedate the point. Record your observations in your Treatment Log, and monitor your dog's condition during your next maintenance treatment.

▸ Check all Ting Points for excessive and deficient characteristics. If you find an imbalance in one or more of these points, sedate or tonify each point in response to what the point evinces. Some practitioners find that balancing only the Ting Points is sufficient for treating many conditions.

▸ If your dog does not exhibit excessive or deficient areas or reactive points that indicate a disharmony, enjoy his good health and move to Closing. (See Chapter Seven, Acupresssure Treatments for Specific Conditions, for further Point Work.)

Closing

▸ Close your dog, working from front to rear, top to bottom by gliding your hand over the Bladder meridian. See Chapter Three, Step-by-Step Canine Acupressure Treatment, for a detailed description of the Closing technique.

Stretches

▸ Shoulder Extension
▸ Buttocks Stretch
▸ Back Stretch

For complete descriptions of each stretch turn to Chapter Six Canine Stretches.

GLOSSARY

ABDUCTOR MUSCLES The muscles that pull a limb away from the central axis of the body.

ACCUMULATION POINTS Specific acupressure points located on a meridian where the Chi accumulates. Used primarily for acute conditions, especially if pain is present.

ACUPOINTS Specific points located on a meridian where the Chi energy flows close to the surface of the body. Stimulation, tonification, sedation and other techniques can be employed to manipulate the Chi energy of the body at these locations.

ACUPRESSURE An ancient healing art that moves and balances Chi energy by use of pressure applied at specific acupoints along the meridian system. Used to release muscular pain, tension, to increase circulation and treat a variety of ailments and conditions by balancing life force energy.

ACUPUNCTURE The manipulation of Chi energy by use of needle insertions at specific acupoints along the meridian system. Used to release muscular pain, tension, to increase circulation and treat a variety of ailments and conditions by balancing life force energy.

ACUTE A condition having a short and relatively sudden course, not long term.

ADDUCTOR MUSCLE The muscles that pull an appendage toward the central axis of the body.

ALARM POINTS Used as indicators of organ and meridian problems. Tenderness at an Alarm Point gives the practitioner an indication of meridian blockage or organ involvement. Alarm Points are used in conjunction with the Association Points.

ALPHA DOG The dominant dog, the pack leader.

ANTIINFLAMMATORY An agent that relieves inflammation of the tissues.

ARTERY The blood vessel carrying blood away from the heart into the system. The blood vessels furnish oxygen and nutrients to the body tissues.

ASPIRIN POINT An acupoint located on the Bladder meridian, Bl 60, known for its ability to reduce pain throughout the body.

ASSISTANCE DOG A dog trained to help physically challenged individuals. Hearing, guide and alarms dogs are types of assistance dogs.

ASSOCIATED MERIDIANS A pair of Yin and Yang meridians. Each of the twelve major meridians has an associated meridian partner, making a total of six paired meridians. Point Work on either of the paired meridians serves to balance the energy flow of the other.

ASSOCIATION POINTS Specific points located along the first channel of the Bladder meridian. Each of the twelve major meridians has a unique Association Point. Association Points can indicate a blockage in the corresponding meridian and are used in conjunction with the Alarm Points to help identify the level of organ involvement.

ATROPHY Decrease in size of muscle or organ resulting from lack of use or disease.

AUTOIMMUNE DISEASE A condition in which the white blood cells destroy the tissues of the organism that created them.

AXIAL SKELETON The part of the skeleton consisting of the spinal column and skull.

BARREL The ribcage of the dog.

BELLY The abdomen or ventral region of the body from the xiphoid cartilage of the sternum to the edge of the pelvis.

BICEPS FEMORIS The two headed muscle located in the upper hind leg.

BIOKINETICS The study of the movement of animals.

BLADDER MERIDIAN One of the twelve major meridians. It is a Yang meridian and is paired with the Kidney meridian, a Yin energy meridian. The Association Points are located on the Bladder meridian.

BREASTBONE The ventral bone to which the ribs attach, sternum or breast plate.

BLOAT A disease common in large breeds of dogs where the stomach twists on the long axis. Also known as gastric torsion or gastric dilation..

CARPAL JOINT The wrist or fore pastern. A complex joint between the distal ends of the radius and ulna and the metacarpal bones.

CARTILAGE The elastic material that covers the articular surfaces of joints.

CHANNEL CHI The aspect of Chi that flows through the meridian or channel system. It is the aspect of Chi that is most available for adjustment or influence by acupressure or acupuncture.

CHEST The external anatomical region of the ribs or thorax.

CHI ENERGY Life force energy which is present in all of nature. There are a variety of "types" of Chi, defined by location and function.

CHRONIC A condition that persists for a long time with little change or improvement.

CLOSING The third phase of an acupressure treatment. The Closing serves to connect the energy flow between the points stimulated during the treatment. It also helps repattern cellular memory and relieve chronic pain.

CLOSING TECHNIQUES Specific techniques used by the acupressure practitioner to complete the Closing phase of an acupressure treatment. Techniques include smooth hand and cupped hand.

COMMAND POINT Also known as "Element" points. Command Points are employed when referencing the Five-Element Theory to either tonify or sedate, based on the Control and Creation Cycle.

CONCEPTION VESSEL One of the eight Extraordinary Vessels. A Yin vessel passing unilaterally along the ventral midline.

CONNECTING POINTS These points connect the Yin and Yang energies of the sister meridians. These points help resolve blockages between the sister meridians. Also known as "Luo" Points.

CONTROL CYCLE The sequence of the Five-Element Theory in which each element controls another and is itself controlled by another element. This sequence helps ensure that a balance is maintained among the five elements.

CREATION CYCLE The sequence of the Five-Element Theory in which each element creates another and is itself created by another element. This sequence helps ensure that a balance is maintained among the five elements.

DEFICIENCY A condition of insufficiency or too little of something. In TCM a deficiency often refers to insufficient energy, indicating the need to improve or increase energy in that area.

DEWCLAW The inside toe on a dog's leg corresponding to the human thumb. It is a vestigial digit.

DIGITS The toes of a dog.

DISTAL POINTS Acupressure points located a distance from the area they benefit.

DOMINANCE The assertive characteristics and nature of a dog.

ELBOW The hinge joint connecting the humerus to the radius and ulna.

ESTROUS The entire reproductive cycle of the dog. Regularly occurring periods during which a female is sexually active and receptive.

EXCESS A condition of surplus or too much of something. In TCM an excess often refers to an over-abundance of energy, indicating the need to decrease or disperse the energy in that area.

EXTRAORDINARY VESSELS Eight Vessels which act as reservoirs of energy for the major meridians. They absorb energy from the major meridians or transfer energy to the major meridians as needed.

FEMUR The large bone that extends down from the coxofemoral joint of the pelvis to the stifle.

FEVER An abnormally high body temperature. In dogs a body temperature of over 101.5 to 102.5 degrees.

FIBULA The smaller of the two bones of the lower hind leg that extend from the stifle to the hock.

FLANKS The portion of the dog's body located between the hind ribs the rear legs.

FOOD CHI Life force energy (Chi) obtained from food.

FOOT PAD The primary weight-bearing pad of each foot, the metacarpal pad of the foreleg and the metatarsal pad of the hind leg.

FOREARM The lower foreleg, between the elbow and carpus.

FOREPASTERN The anatomical region between the carpus and the toes.

FOREPAW The front foot.

FOREQUARTERS The shoulders and the anterior limbs

FU ORGANS The six Yang organs, also referred to as the hollow organs.

GAIT The manner or style of locomotion. Used often to assess the soundness of an animal. Gait includes the walk, trot, lop, pace, canter and gallop.

GALL BLADDER MERIDIAN One of the twelve major meridians. It is a Yang meridian and is paired with the Liver meridian, a Yin energy meridian.

GASTROINTESTINAL Pertaining to the stomach and intestines. It can refer to the entire digestive tract.

GOVERNING VESSEL One of the Eight Extraordinary Vessels. This is a Yang vessel that runs uni-laterally along the dorsal midline.

HAMSTRING The tendon of the biceps femoris muscle of the hind leg.

HAUNCH The region of the hips and buttocks.

HEART MERIDIAN One of the twelve major meridians. It is a Yin meridian and is paired with the Small Intestine meridian, a Yang energy meridian.

HINDQUARTERS The anatomical body area located behind the flanks and includes the pelvis, thighs and hocks.

HIP JOINT The joint between the femur and the pelvis.

HIP SOCKET The pelvic cavity into which fits the head of the femur and with which it articulates.

HOCK The ankle joint of quadripeds. The tarsus or joint between the stifle and pastern.

HUMERUS The upper arm bone, that which extends from the shoulder to the elbow.

ILIUM The pelvic bone on which the hip socket is located. It connects to the sacral vertebrae at the sacroiliac junction.

INFLUENTIAL POINTS Points which affect a particular functional system.

INTERVERTEBRAL DISK The cushioning structure located between the bodies of adjacent vertebrae.

JING The life essence, or material aspect of Chi, a fundamental substance.

KIDNEY MERIDIAN One of the twelve major meridians. It is a Yin meridian and is paired with the Bladder meridian, a Yang energy meridian.

KNEECAP The patella. A sesmoid bone located on the anterior surface of the stifle joint.

KNUCKLE The metacarpal or metatarsal joint. The dorsal surface of any foot joint.

LAME An irregularity or impairment of the function of locomotion or gaits.

LARGE INTESTINE MERIDIAN One of the twelve major meridians. It is a Yang meridian and is paired with the Lung meridian, a Yin energy meridian.

LATERAL Toward the outside of the body.

LIGAMENTS Connective tissue that binds joints together and connects bones and cartilage.

LIVER MERIDIAN One of the twelve major meridians. It is a Yin meridian and is paired with the Gall Bladder meridian, a Yang energy meridian.

LOCAL POINTS Acupressure points located in the area they benefit.

LOIN The anatomical area of the back between the last rib and the pelvis.

LONG LINE a 25 to 50 foot lease used for dog training.

LUMBAR Pertaining to the loins, the part of the back between the thorax and pelvis.

LUMBOSACRAL JOINT Located at the top of the croup, it rotates the hindquarters and pelvis forward under the body.

LUNG CHI Life energy (Chi) which is extracted from the air.

LUNG MERIDIAN One of the twelve major meridians. It is a Yin meridian and is paired with the Large Intestine meridian, a Yang energy meridian.

MASTER POINT Acupoints which powerfully affect a regional area of the body. There are six Master Points.

MEDIAL Toward the center of the body.

MERIDIAN BLOCKAGE A condition which impedes the smooth, even and balanced flow of Chi energy throughout the meridian system.

MERIDIAN SYSTEM The network of invisible but real channels through which the Chi (life force) energy flows throughout the body. These channels are connected and influence each other.

MERIDIANS Individual channels that are part of a network through which Chi energy flows throughout the body. There are twelve major meridians in all animals.

METACARPUS The bones leading from the carpus or wrist to the toes.

METATARSUS The bones leading from the tarsus or hock to the toes.

OPENING The first phase of an acupressure treatment. The Opening introduces "structured" touch to the animal. The Opening also affords the practitioner the opportunity to identify areas of the body which may need Point Work.

ORIGINAL CHI The fixed amount of Chi given at conception. Also known as Source Chi.

PALPATION Feeling or perceiving by the sense of touch.

PASTERN The region of the metatarsus extending from the hock to the foot in the hind leg and the metacarpal area of the foreleg.

PATELLA Kneecap. A large sesamoid bone at the femorotibial joint.

PAW Any of the dog's four feet.

PECTORAL Pertaining to the chest or breast area.

PELVIC LIMB Either hind leg.

PELVIS The bony girdle comprised of the Ilium, ischium and pubis.

PERICARDIUM MERIDIAN One of the twelve major meridians. It is a Yin meridian and is paired with the Triple Heater meridian, a Yang energy meridian.

POINT WORK The stimulation of acupoints located along the meridian system.

POINT WORK TECHNIQUES The procedures used to stimulate points. There are several techniques a practitioner may use, each of which has a unique quality.

PROTECTIVE CHI The Chi that protects the body from harmful external forces.

PROXIMAL Nearer to or toward the center, or midline, of the body.

RADIUS One of the two bones of the forearm which extends from the elbow to the carpus.

RECOVERY TIME In competition, the time required for a dog's pulse and respiration to return to normal.

SEDATE To disperse or decrease.

SEDATION POINT Points which subdue an excess of energy within the meridian flow.

SEPARATION ANXIETY A feeling of apprehension or agitation of some dogs when their person leaves them for a period of time. More commonly seen when dogs are left in new environments.

SCAPULA The shoulder blade.

SHEN Represents the "spirit" aspect of Chi energy.

SHOCK A condition of acute peripheral circulatory failure due to derangement of circulatory control or loss of circulating fluid.

SKELETON The bony framework of the body. There are 310 bones in the skeleton of the female dog and 311 in the male's framework.

SMALL INTESTINE MERIDIAN One of the twelve major meridians. It is a Yang meridian and is paired with the Heart meridian, a Yin energy meridian.

SOURCE POINTS A specific point directly connected to each of the twelve major meridians. The Source Point can either sedate or tonify, depending upon the need of the meridian at the time of stimulation.

SPINOUS PROCESSES The upward projections of each vertebrae.

SPLEEN MERIDIAN One of the twelve major meridians. It is a Yin meridian and is paired with the Stomach meridian, a Yang energy meridian.

STIFLE The "knee" on the hind leg of the dog.

STOMACH MERIDIAN One of the twelve major meridians. It is a Yang meridian and is paired with the Spleen, a Yin energy meridian.

TENDONS Tissue that connects muscle to bone, they are strong and inelastic.

THERAPY DOG A specially trained dog used in the treatment of humans for mental, physical,or psychological illnesses.

THIGH The region of hind leg that lies above the stifle and below the hip.

THORACIC VERTEBRAE The thirteen bones that form the top of the rib cage.

TIBIA The lower leg bone extending from the stifle to the tarsus.

TING POINT Located at the toes of the dog's front and hind legs. There is one Ting Point for each meridian. Used to balance the energy of the meridian and for other specific conditions.

TONIFICATION POINTS A specific acupoint located on each of twelve major meridians. Stimulation of these points tonifies or adds energy to that meridian.

TONIFY To increase or strengthen.

TRIPLE HEATER One of the twelve major meridians. It is a Yang meridian and is paired with the Pericardium meridian, a Yin energy meridian.

ULNA A bone of the foreleg which extends from the elbow joint to the carpus.

UPPER ARM The anatomical area between the elbow and the shoulder.

VASCULAR SYSTEM Blood vessel network of the body.

VERTEBRAE The spinal column consisting of 7 cervical, 13 thoracic, 7 lumbar 3 sacral and 1 to 22 cocygeal vertebrae.

WRIST The complex joint between the radius and ulna and the metacarpals.

YANG Part of the Yin/Yang duality. Some attributes associated with Yang include: warmth, outer, sunny side, movement, acute, light, male.

YIN Part of the Yin/Yang duality. Some attributes associated with Yin include: cold, inner, shady side, substance, chronic, dark, female.

ZANG The six Yin organs, also referred to as the solid organs

BIBLIOGRAPHY

Altman, Sheldon, DVM. *An Introduction to Acupuncture for Animals.* Chen's Corporation, Monterey Park, CA. 1981.

Beinfield, Harriet, L.Ac. & Korngold, Efrem, L. Ac., OMD. *Between Heaven and Earth, A Guide to Chinese Medicine.* Ballentine Books, New York, NY. 1991.

Birch, Stephen and Matsumoto, Kiiko, *Five Elements and Ten Stems.* Paradigm Publications, Brookline, MA 1983.

Blood, D.C.and Studdert, Virginia. *Bailliere's Comprehensive Veterinary Dictionary.* Bailliere Tindall, London, 1998.

Cohen, Misha Ruth, OMD, Lac. *The Chinese Way to Healing: Many Paths to Wholeness.* A Perigree Book, The Berkley Publishing Group, New York, NY, 1996.

Connelly, Dianne, M., Ph.D., M. Ac. *Traditional Acupuncture: The Law of the Five Elements.* The Centre for Traditional Acupuncture, Columbia, MD. 1989.

Dodman, Dr. Nicholas. *The Dog Who Loved Too Much,* Bantam Books, 1996.

Donaldson, Jean. *The Culture Clash.* James and Kenneth Publishers, Berkeley, CA 1996.

Fox, Michad W. Ph.D., D.Sc. *The Healing Touch.* New Market Press, New York, NY. 1990.

Gach, Michael Reed, *Acupressure's Potent Points, A Guide to Self-Of Care for Common Ailments.* Bantam Books, New York, NY 1990.

Gerber, Richard, MD. *Vibrational Medicine.* Bear & Co., Santa Fe, NM. 1988.

International Veterinarian Acupuncture Society (IVAS), *IVAS Course Manual 6ᵗʰ Edition*, IVAS, United States, 1997.

International Veterinary Acupuncture Society, *The Chinese Acupuncture, 5,000 Year Old Oriental Art of Healing.*

Kaptchuk, Ted, OMD. *The Web That Has No Weaver, Understanding Chinese Medicine.* Congdon & Weed, Inc., New York, NY.

McClellan, Sam. *Integrative Acupressure.* Perigree Books, 1998.

Maciocia, Giovanni, CaC. *The Foundations of Chinese Medicine, A Comprehensive Text for Acupuncturists and Herbalists.* Churchill Livingstone. New York, NY 1989.

Martin, Ann N. *Foods Pets Die For.* New Sage Press, Oregon, 1997.

Mason, Jeffrey Moussaieff. *Dogs Never Lie About Love.* Three Rivers Press, New York, NY 1997.
Mann, Felix, MB. *Acupuncture, The Ancient Chinese Art of Healing and How It Works Scientifically.* Vintage Books, New York, NY. 1973.

Namokoshi, Tory. *The Complete Book of Shiatsu Therapy.* Japan Publications Inc., New York & Tokyo. 1981.

Pitcairn, Richard H., DVM, MS. *Natural Health for Dogs and Cats.* Rodale Press, Emmaus, PA 1982.

Rice, Dan, DVM. *Dogs From A to Z, A Dictionary of Canine Terms. Barron's Educational Series,* Hauppauge, NY, 1998.

Serizawa, Katsusuke. *Tsubo Vital Points for Oriental Therapy.* Japan Publications Inc., Tokyo & New York. 1976.

Schoen,Allen,M. *Veterinary Acupuncture, Ancient Art to Modern Medicine.* American Veterinary Publications, Inc., Goleta, CA. 1994.

Schoen, Allen M., DVM, MS and Wynn, Susan, DVM. *Complimentary and Alternative Veterinary Medicine.* Mosby 1998.

Schwartz, Cheryl, DVM. *Four Paws Five Directions, A Guide to Chinese Medicine for Cats and Dogs.* Celestial Arts, Berkeley, CA, 1996.

Sohn, Tina Amma, *The Ancient Art of Oriental Healing.* Healing Arts Press, Rochester, Vermont. 1988.

Stein, Diane. *Natural Healing for Dogs and Cats.* The Crossing Press, Freedom, CA. 1993.

Stux, Gabriel, & Pomeranz, Bruce. *Basics of Acupuncture.* Springer-Verlag, Berlin, Heidelberg, New York. 1991.

Zidonis, Nancy, A. Snow, Amy and Soderberg, Marie K. *Equine Acupressure: A Working Manual.* Tallgrass Publishers, LLC, Denver, CO 1998.

Books in print by Dr. Michael W. Fox:
Beyond Evolution: The Genetically Altered Future of Plants, Animals, the Earth…and Humans. (1999)
Concepts in Ethology:Animal Behavior and Bioethics. (second edition) (1998)
The Boundless Circle: Caring For Creatures and Creation (1996)
You Can Save The Animals: 50 Things You Can Do Now (1991)
Supercat: Raising The Perfect Feline Companion (1990)
Superdog: Raising the Perfect Canine Companion (1990)\The Healing Touch: Massage Therapy for Cats and Dogs (1983)

TALLGRASS ANIMAL ACUPRESSURE TRAINING PROGRAMS

Tallgrass has been serving the human and animal community for over 13 years through acupressure manuals, meridian charts, videos and training. We are constantly expanding our programs and products to increase everyone's knowledge of acupressure and other forms of vibrational medicine. Our intent is to provide the best learning tools and training programs to give animal guardians, trainers, and healthcare practitioners access to powerful healing.

Tallgrass offers highly interactive training programs in acupressure and other vibrational medicine modalities for animals. Our instructors are experienced and known as leaders in their field. We are consistently adding new learning opportunities. Participants receive a certificate of completion after passing an examination and submitting case studies.

Some of our expanding course offerings include:

Acupressure	Essential Oils / Aromatherapy
Homeopathy	Magnetic Therapy
Reiki	Botanical and Herbal Remedy
Jin Shin Energy	Flower Essences

Distance Learning Program

For continued training, continuing education units, and a certificate program, Tallgrass works with associations and accredited educational institutions to offer online and correspondence programs. These courses include readings, written assignments, and case studies. Some of the courses are:

Traditional Chinese Medicine	Acupoint Classification
The Meridian Theory	Aromatherapy
Five-Element Theory	Vibrational Medicine Electives

Secondary Courses

For further hands-on course work, Tallgrass offers more in-depth courses in acupressure treatment and other modalities. These clinics are designed to give participants greater understanding and particular skills in a selected field.

The canine clinic was Awesome. How could you take something so complex and give a great overview in three days! Thank you, it was great and what we didn't cover in depth was supplied with good additional reading and studying.

- Lee Deaton, Bartlett, Illinois

Brilliant Courses! All of us learned so much about how to really care for our horses and dogs.

-Karen Bourdon, Oxfordshire, England

For further information or to host a clinic contact
Animal Acupressure www.animalacupressure.com
Call toll free 888.841.7211 or email acupressure4all@earthlink.net

AUTHOR PROFILES

Photo by Jan Jones

The Well Connected Dog: A Guide to Canine Acupressure is the collaborative effort of Nancy Zidonis and Amy Snow. Each has contributed their talents, skills and knowledge with the intent of making acupressure accessible to everyone to enjoy with their dogs. In 1998, Nancy and Amy published their first book together entitled *Equine Acupressure: A Working Manual*.

Nancy Zidonis was the initial force behind the book. During the past ten years, she has co-authored two other acupressure texts and developed equine, canine and feline meridian charts. She is a founding board member of the International Alliance of Animal Therapists and Healers.

As a child in rural Ohio, Nancy thoroughly enjoyed being with animals. She gained an abiding respect for the integrity of horses, dogs and cats. She lives on a farm in rural Colorado with her horse, Sara and her dog, Josie.

Amy Snow has combined her professional publications background and experience in the healing arts with her love of all animals in co-authoring this book. She began her dog-care career at the age of ten. When growing up in New York City neighbors asked her to walk their dogs after school. With an Irish wolfhound on one side of her and a Borzoi on the other, she would walk for hours on the streets of Lower manhattan and Washington square Park. People would stare at the spectacle of the little girl with two gentle giants.

Amy lives in rural Colorado with her Golden Retriever, Oak, a Delta Society Therapy Assistance Dog, and a Chesapeake Bay Retriever, Shayna Maidel.

Nancy and Amy are working with Hocking College in Nelsonville, Ohio to develop an accredited animal acupressure curriculum. Contact Tallgrass Animal Acupressure for further information regarding training.

Notes

order form

CANINE

The Well-Connected Dog: A Guide to Canine Acupressure.(ISBN 0-9645982-4-8) $25.95
Canine Meridian Chart. 12 x 18 color, laminated chart. $16.00

EQUINE

Equine Acupressure, A Working Manual. (ISBN 0-9645982-2-1) $29.95

Equine Meridian Chart. 12x18 color, laminated chart. $16.00

Equine Stretch Poster. 12x18 laminated poster. $16.00

Five-Element Meridian Chart Set. Includes 4 - 12x18 color, laminated charts of meridian system: Twelve Major Meridians, Governing and Conception Vessels, Accumulation, Alarm, Association, Command, Connecting, Source, and Ting Points. Plus Five-Element Theory chart. $53.50

New! Equine Acupressure Video - 50 minute Instructional Introductory Tape, companion to the Equine Acupressure Book. $33.95

FELINE

Acu-Cat: A Guide to Feline Acupressure. (ISBN 0-9645982-5-1) $23.95

Feline Meridian Chart. 12 x 18 color, laminated chart. $16.00

Ordered By:	Ship to: (If Different)
Name:	Name:
Street/POB:	Street/POB:
City/Zip:	City/Zip:

DESCRIPTION	QTY	PRICE	TOTAL AMT.

Shipping & Handling (Canada + $8.00)
1-2 Books $5.00   3-6 Books   8.00
1-3 Charts   5.00   4-6 Charts   8.00

Subtotal (USA Funds)	
CO Res. 3.8%	
S & H	
TOTAL	

PAYMENT TO TALLGRASS PUBLISHERS, LLC.:

VISA/MC#   Expiration Date:

TO ORDER: FAX: 303.681.2999 / Email: tallgrasspub@earthlink.net / CALL 888.841.7211
SEND TO: Tallgrass Publishers, 4559 W. Red Rock Dr. Larkspur, CO 80118
website: www.tallgrasspublshers.com or www.animalacupressure.com

166